THE WORLD'S CHRISTMAS

Olive Wyon

The World's Christmas

Illustrated by Peter Barrett

SCM PRESS LTD
BLOOMSBURY STREET LONDON

FIRST PUBLISHED 1964
© SCM PRESS LTD 1964
PRINTED IN GREAT BRITAIN BY
BILLING AND SONS LTD
GUILDFORD AND LONDON

CONTENTS

6   CONTENTS

INTRODUCTION

The Meaning of Christmas

I

THE aim of this book is to show the significance of
Christmas at the deepest level. It is mainly a book for
adults, *not* for children, although it contains some
children's stories. Some years ago *Punch* satirized the growing
secularization of Christmas in a scene in which a man ex-
claims: 'I don't know what we're coming to! They are even
bringing religion into Christmas nowadays!' Many of the
stories here presented—whether they are fact or fiction—
show the profound meaning of Christmas to people in great
straits: facing prison, exile, loss, and death; and this meaning
is for the whole world.

The book opens with a story called *The Emperor's Vision*.
It is based upon a legend which grew out of the belief that
Virgil's Fourth Eclogue was a direct prophecy of the birth of
Christ. Here are some lines from Dryden's version:

The last great Age, foretold by sacred Rimes
Renews its finished course. . . . A Golden progeny
From Heaven descends. The Father banished virtue shall
    restore. . . .
The Son shall lead the life of Gods, and be
By Gods and Heroes seen . . .
The jarring nations He in peace shall bind,
And with paternal virtues rule mankind.
Unbidden Earth shall wreathing ivy bring
And fragrant herbs (the promises of Spring)
As her first offerings to her infant King.

This poem was taken over wholesale as a foreshadowing of Christ. It was quoted by Constantine when he was addressing the whole Christian population of the Empire, on the occasion of the establishment of Christianity as the State religion. Whatever Virgil really meant 'it remains true that Virgil . . . was reflecting a feeling, widespread in the Mediterranean and Middle Eastern area, that a Saviour was about to come and rid the world of the miseries into which it had fallen'.[1] This prophecy of Virgil had an immense influence upon many generations.

These stories fall naturally into three groups. The first group is intended for younger children, i.e. children at the imaginative stage, when they have a feeling for mystery and fairy tales, and for legends with an underlying meaning. This period of childhood cannot be exactly estimated in terms of age; it depends both upon temperament and on environment.

The second group is distinctly adult. Many of these stories are grim. This is due to the fact that they spring out of the personal experience of men and women suffering under the Hitler régime in Germany, or under Czarist rule in a bygone Russia. Some reflect the beliefs of past ages in Northern Europe, as well as tragic war memories from Poland. Incidentally, one striking point emerged while I was going through the material which I had collected in Germany in 1938, and what I found in Germany after the War. The 1938 material was so trivial, often sentimental, and out-of-date (even then) that I could use none of it. All the impressive incidents and stories come out of the tragic experiences of war, defeat, and post-war depression. They have a sense of stark reality.

The third group comes from Africa and Asia. Here, to some extent, these stories reflect an early stage in the history of Christian missions. It is a far cry from them to a fairly recent account of a Christmas Day on the coast of New Guinea. Here Papuan children, after worship in church, gathered on the sea-shore for water-sports, and had a 'merry Christmas'. From this small village they sent a gift of £5 to the World

[1] Michael Grant, *Roman Literature*, p. 169.

Council of Churches at Geneva for refugees in Europe. This section closes with a description of an act of worship in Central Africa, in which Africans and Europeans united, in the presence of wondering pagans. This simple story is a foreshadowing of that Day of the Lord when all will be one in Christ, for 'we sing our common Lord'. For in that day Chesterton's vision will be fulfilled, when

> to an open house in the evening
> Home shall all men come,
> To an older place than Eden
> And a taller town than Rome. . . .
> To the place where God was homeless
> And all men are at home.

II

When did the celebration of the Christmas festival begin? It is strange to learn that for the first three centuries Christians did not celebrate it at all. Why was this? It was because their interest was wholly centred on Jesus as the Crucified and Exalted Lord. They had not begun to think about the Incarnation. But as time went on, and Christian thinkers began to reflect more deeply upon the Person of our Lord, they began to see the significance of the Incarnation. Eastern Christians, in particular, began to think a great deal about 'the mystery of God's entry into the world in a human person'.[1] As their interest in the 'historical Jesus' deepened, instinctively the Church began to celebrate Christmas with joy and splendour. The earliest Christmas liturgy that has yet been discovered is an Egyptian papyrus of the beginning of the fourth century. The number of fingerprints on this fragment show that it had been much used. It opens with readings from the Gospels: about Christ's birth at Bethlehem, the flight into Egypt, and the return to Nazareth, with the sung response:

[1] Oscar Cullmann, *The Early Church*, p. 24.

Born at Bethlehem,
Brought up at Nazareth,
Dwelt in Galilee.

This was followed by the story of the visit of the Magi, to which the choir sang the response:

We have seen a sign from heaven,
The shining star.

Then the priest read the Nativity Story from the Gospel of Luke and the choir sang:

Shepherds in the field were amazed,
They fell on their knees and sang:
Glory to the Father, Hallelujah!
Glory to the Son, and to the Holy Ghost!
  Hallelujah! Hallelujah! Hallelujah!

This was how the birth of Christ was celebrated at the beginning of the fourth century, on the night of January 6th to 7th.

But why on January 6th? To understand this we have to go back a little way. In the second century there was a heretical sect—the followers of the Alexandrian Gnostic Basilides—which celebrated the Baptism of Christ on January 6th or 10th. Their view was that the divine Christ only 'appeared on earth' at the Baptism of Jesus. So this festival was called 'Epiphany' or 'appearing'. Apparently this sect chose this date because on the night of January 5th-6th the waters of the Nile were supposed to have magical powers. The orthodox Christians, on the other hand, did not believe that Christ's first 'appearing' was at his Baptism, but they appreciated the importance of that event, so they chose January 6th in order to combine the memory of his 'appearing' at his Baptism with that of his birth. For a long time the feast of the Epiphany was celebrated in Palestine with great magnificence.

Why then was the date of the Christmas festival changed, later on, from January 6th to December 25th? The reasons for this change are not yet quite clear; perhaps they never will be. 'The most probable assumption', says Cullmann, 'is that this took place in Rome between A.D. 325 and 354, after the older Epiphany festival had already come from the east to the west, possibly even to Rome. December 25th is attested in Rome as the date of Christ's birth in the year A.D. 336, and must have been observed as such, even before this, under Constantine the Great.'[1]

December 25th was chosen because it coincided with the great pagan festival in honour of the Sun, the 'unconquered Sun-God'. The Christian leaders felt that it was fitting that the festival of light should be 'baptized into Christ', the Light of the world. 'Christ is *our* new Sun', said St Ambrose. For a time the merging of the two festivals caused a good deal of confusion of thought, and a certain amount of opposition to the change of date. Professor Cullmann has shown that it was Chrysostom who finally succeeded in establishing, once for all, the date of December 25th as the festival of Christmas.

III

When the festival of Christmas took root in Europe, gradually a wealth of poetry, music, drama, legend, and popular customs gathered round it. Traces of these beliefs and customs can be found in many of the stories in this book, for we are in the European tradition. We too have a pagan past: many of our traditional customs come from that source. For instance, the emphasis on light, greenery, and even on present-giving is inherited from the solar background of the winter festival, and the observance of the Kalends of January, the Roman New Year.

The Christmas Tree seems to have come from Germany, but the origin of the custom is obscure. One tradition suggests that it was due to the action of St Boniface, the 'Apostle of Germany', in the eighth century, when he cut down the sacred oak dedicated to Odin, in the presence of scandalized villagers,

[1] *The Early Church*, p. 29.

and in its stead dedicated a fir tree to the Holy Child. At any rate, the Christmas Tree seems to have been known in Germany in the sixteenth century.

There was also a widespread belief that certain trees blossom at Christmas, or bend their branches low in worship. Animals, too, figure largely in these ideas: it was said that cattle and horses on Christmas Eve turn to the East and kneel. The raven was said to be the first to know that the Birth had taken place, but the cock was the first to proclaim the event, *Christus natus est*, and so ever since then, on the Holy Night, the cocks crow all through the night. One delightful touch comes in the suggestion that on that Night 'the bees hum the Hundredth Psalm in their hives'. Christopher Smart gathers up this joy of creation at the Birth of Christ in his poem on *The Nativity of Our Lord*:

> Spinks and ousels sing sublimely
> 'We too have a Saviour born';
> Whiter blossoms burst untimely
> On the blest Mosaic thorn.

In many parts of Europe ghost stories were very popular at this season. One tradition is that no 'spirit' may walk abroad on this Holy Night. In *Hamlet*,

> Some say that ever 'gainst that season comes
> Wherein our Saviour's birth is celebrated,
> The bird of dawning singeth all night long.
> And then, they say, no spirit dare stir abroad
> The nights are wholesome, then no planets strike,
> No fairy takes nor witch has power to harm,
> So hallowed and so gracious is the time.

Another tradition, especially in Scandinavia, was that the trolls were abroad on Christmas Night, and everyone stayed indoors. Here too the great Christmas Candle was lit at dusk on Christmas Eve and extinguished at sunrise.

As a rule in Europe the Feast of the Epiphany (January 6th) ends the Christmas season—hence the expression, 'the twelve days of Christmas'. But at one time the final festival was

Candlemas (February 2nd), commemorating the Presentation
of Christ in the Temple. Candles were (and still are) carried
round the church in procession while choir and people sing of
him who came as a 'Light to lighten the Gentiles' (all nations)
and then—we look to the Spring. Herrick wrote:

> Down with the rosemary and bays,
> Down with the mistletoe. . . .
> Until the dancing Easter Day,
> Or Easter Eve appear.

IV

Traditional customs are interesting; some of them are
significant, especially those that reflect the wonder of child-
like people who are dimly aware of the wonder of Christ's
coming and its effect on the universe as a whole. Naturally
their instinct was to express this joy in music and song. And
this element in the Christmas Festival is still very popular
(outside the Church as well as inside) in the form of carol-
singing. What, however, is a 'carol'? It is neither a hymn nor
a poem; it has a special quality which is not easy to describe.
We can only begin to understand it when we learn something
of its history.

The word 'carol' seems to be derived from the Greek word
choros, which means first of all a dance (a choral dance), then
a *company* of dancers, and finally a *chorus* or *choir*. 'Dance
is at the heart of it', says Dr Erik Routley; 'it began as a dance.
We shall never understand its extraordinary history if we
forget that it began not as a pious religious gesture, but as a
dance.'[1] Now dancing was part of worship in antiquity, and
the early Church took this element into its own worship: we
read of 'dancing in the choir' and of bishops who led the dance
on feast days. Some of the early Fathers said 'the angels were
always dancing' and that 'the glorious *company* of the

[1] *The English Carol*, p. 27.

Apostles' was really a choir of dancers. Later on this custom fell into disrepute, but for a good while longer, in some countries, the custom lingered on, especially in cathedrals. During this early period the Church had boldly taken over and used the tunes and dances which were prevalent in the world around. They seem to have agreed with the opinion of the Salvationist who said: 'Why should the devil have all the best tunes?' But this early period was followed by the collapse of the Roman Empire and the long dark tunnel of the so-called Dark Ages. A very puritan spirit came over the Church leaders and they frowned upon music and drama and, more than all, upon dancing. The Liturgy, however, developed and this led to a kind of drama out of which came the mystery plays, so much loved in the Middle Ages. This process led to the development of religious songs, like the Coventry Carol; gradually folk-songs and dance tunes took the place of the former liturgical music, and 'the time was ripe for the carol'.

Percy Dearmer suggests that the carol did not appear in Christian history 'until the modern spirit of humanism had dawned upon the Middle Ages'. It reached its peak in the fifteenth century. Most of our old carols in this country come from the two and a half centuries between 1400 and 1647. Then the old carols went underground. For a time it seemed as though they had been lost for ever. But the tradition lingered on out of sight. In the second half of the nineteenth century some of the ancient carols were re-discovered. In 1871 a second period of carol revival in England was ushered in by the publication of Christmas Carols New and Old by Bramley and Stainer. This was followed in the early years of the twentieth century by the Cowley Carol Book by Dr G. R. Woodward. The publication of the Oxford Book of Carols, which contains a number of carols from other parts of Europe, was a great event. This book, and the establishment of the Service of Nine lessons and Carols at King's College, Cambridge, have fostered and increased the love of carols, which are now more popular than ever.

But almost no new carols are being written in this country.

Why is this? Can it be that we have trivialized and external-ized Christmas to such an extent that in many families the children hear so much about 'Santa Claus' and the 'Baby Jesus' that every breath of mystery and wonder has been blown away? Or is it that we are too proud and too sophisti-cated to accept the truth of God in such a simple and homely guise? Or have we forgotten that there *is* a meaning behind it all? If this be so no amount of carol-singing and giving to charity will help us to find the meaning. For that we have to face the fact of Jesus Christ. He alone is the meaning of Christmas.

But it is no wonder that we feel baffled. For here, at the centre of the Christian faith, we are confronted by paradox. Paradox in this connexion has been defined as 'a truly religious mystery, close to experience and to faith'.[1] Paradox runs right through the whole of the Christian message. Yet all down the centuries the mystery that lies behind and within the doctrine has been 'grasped by countless unsophisticated Christian men and women in the actual life of faith'; and not only by so-called 'simple' people either, for by whatever road we come to a personal faith, all alike we bow in humility and reverence before a mystery greater than our human minds can ever fathom. In the best of the old carols there is a wonderful blending of mystery and humanity: the Holy God who is infinitely beyond us, and *Emmanuel*, 'God with us', ' manifest in the flesh'. The Good News, which is for all nations, is thus both 'other-worldly' and 'this-worldly': because

God all bounteous, all creative,
Whom no ills from good dissuade,
Is incarnate, and a native
Of the very world He made.

But we miss the full meaning of Christmas if we do not link it up with the whole of the Gospel Story, including the Passion and the Resurrection. Nowhere is this more profoundly or

[1] D. Baillie, *God was in Christ*, p. 107.

humanly expressed than in an old carol[1] which begins with the words:

Tomorrow shall be my dancing day
I would my true love did so chance
To see the legend of my play
To call my true love to my dance.

It is Christ who is speaking, and the 'legend' is the whole Gospel story down to the Ascension, where he says:

'I dwell on the right hand of God, that man
may come to the general dance.'

And after every verse comes the haunting refrain:

'Sing, O my love, my love, my love,
This have I done for my true love.'

Prayer of St Gregory for Christmas

It is very meet and our bounden duty that we should at all times and in all places give thanks unto thee, Holy Lord, Almighty Father, Eternal God: because by the mystery of the Word made flesh, the light of thy brightness has shone anew upon the eyes of our mind; that, knowing God made visible, we may be caught up to the invisible love. Amen.

[1] *Oxford Carol Book*, No. 71.

1 · The Emperor's Vision

An Ancient Legend

WHEN Augustus was Emperor of Rome and Herod was King in Judaea, a great and holy night came down upon the earth. It was the darkest night that men had known: it was impossible to find one's way even along the most familiar road. The silence was as profound as the darkness. There was no wind, and even the aspen leaves did not quiver. Everything was motionless. It seemed as though all nature feared to break the stillness.

It was a *good* silence: the wild beasts did not roam about the forests seeking their prey; the serpents did not sting, and the dogs did not bark. Now a strange thing happened that night in the great city of Rome. A small group of men came down from the Emperor's palace on the Palatine Hill, and walked quietly through the Forum towards the Capitol. That day the senators had asked the Emperor whether he would

B

be willing for them to erect a temple in his honour on Rome's sacred hill. The Emperor did not answer. He wished to find out from the gods whether it would be right for him to do this. So he and his friends had set out after dark to offer a sacrifice to the gods on the Capitol.

Augustus was now an old man, so he was carried in a litter. In his hands he held the cage of doves for the sacrifice. There were no soldiers or priests with him, no one but his closest friends. Torch-bearers walked in front to show the way, and at the rear of the little procession came the slaves, carrying a tripod, some knives, and charcoal for the sacred fire. As they went along the Emperor talked cheerfully with his friends; they did not notice the unusual stillness.

It was only when they reached the summit of the Capitol, and stood still, that they began to realize that this was a very unusual night. They wondered what it could mean. Then, a little way ahead, they saw a strange sight: at first they thought it was a twisted olive tree, growing on the very edge of the cliff; but when it moved slightly they saw that it was the ancient Sibyl who had lived for many years in a cave near by.

They whispered together: 'Why has she come out of her cave tonight? Has she come to foretell some great event—for the Emperor? Or for the Empire?' They stood still and watched her. She was looking away into the darkness as though she could *see* something happening, although the night was so dark. Augustus and his friends were now deeply impressed by the quietness; and though they would not admit it, some of them were afraid. Then one or two spoke to the Emperor in a low voice: 'It is a good omen', they said; 'it is time to offer the sacrifice.' But though the Emperor held the dove in his hands to make the sacrifice the bird struggled so hard that it escaped and flew away into the night.

Suddenly, the silence was broken: a brilliant star blazed over the sacred hill: all nature awoke: the wind swayed the trees, the sound of the rushing Tiber came up to the little group on the sacred hill; the moon came out, and soon the sky was full of stars. Then, out of the silvery clouds a dove circled down and lighted on the shoulders of Augustus.

The Emperor was filled with joy, and his friends and slaves fell at his feet. 'Hail Caesar!' they cried. 'You are the god to be worshipped on this sacred hill!' They made such a noise that the ancient Sibyl was roused from her trance. She turned towards them and came down among the men; she was such a terrifying sight, with her tangled hair and her blazing eyes, that they fell back in fear and awe. She went forward, clutched the Emperor's hand, and with her other hand she pointed towards the East.

'Look!' she commanded.

And as Augustus looked he too saw a vision: he saw a common stable in a rocky hillside, in an Eastern land; shepherds were kneeling in the entrance to a cave. He saw a young mother with a child on her knees, sitting on a bundle of straw. The Sibyl's big knotty fingers pointed to the Babe: 'Hail Caesar!' she exclaimed with a burst of scornful laughter! 'There is the God who will be worshipped on the Capitol Hill!'

Augustus was horrified, and shrank away from her; he thought she was mad. But the spirit of prophecy fell upon the Sibyl. Her eyes began to burn with a strange light, her hands were stretched up to heaven, and her voice rang out with such power that it could have been heard for miles. And the words she uttered were amazing. She turned towards the Emperor and exclaimed: 'The Redeemer of the world shall be worshipped upon the Capitol Hill—but he will be *Christ*, not a frail mortal.' Then she strode past the terrified men and disappeared from sight.

Next day Augustus met the Senate. He told the senators that he did not wish a temple to be built in his honour on the Capitol. Later, in its place, he built a sanctuary in honour of the new-born Child he had seen in his vision. He named it 'Heaven's Altar'—*Ara Coeli*.

2 · *The First Christmas Tree*

WILL VESPER

A Story from Germany for Children

IT was a cold winter night. Day after day the snow had been falling, and it was still snowing. A bitter East wind was sweeping over the lonely fields and plains, and the cold was piercing. Two men were walking across the flat plain, their heads bent low as they fought their way against the wind. They moved slowly as though they were tired, and evening was drawing on. The whole day had been dull and grey, and now darkness was falling earlier than usual. In the whole wide expanse there was not a tree or a bush to be seen. Here and there a wooden pole sticking up out of the snow marked the line of the road buried beneath the weight of the snow.

One of the men, who was walking ahead of his companion, gave the impression of being young, but his face was scarcely visible, for he was enveloped in a heavy thick mantle, which looked as though it had been made of some old sacking. The other man was equally well wrapped up, though his clothes, too, were poor enough. The younger man pressed on tirelessly, walking with half-closed eyes, almost as though he were in a dream. At last in the distance they saw the dim outline of something which might be a house. The older man called out 'D'you see that?' The other nodded his head, and went on walking. As the two men came nearer they saw that it was a large farm-house, surrounded by outbuildings.

By the time the two travellers had reached the farm-house night had fallen. All around them was the silence of the night,

broken only now and again by sounds from within the house
and the stables; for it seemed to be a large farm, standing by
itself, a little way off the road, and shaded by a few trees. Light
streamed from many of the windows. From the outbuildings
came the homely stable noises: the clatter of chains, the stamp-
ing of hooves, and occasionally the lowing of a cow. By the
time the two travellers had reached the shelter of a wall, they
were out of breath. So they stood still for a few moments to
recover. Then the younger man, who was exhausted, sat down
on an upturned wheelbarrow to rest. A faint gleam of light fell
upon him from a window close at hand. The older man went
towards the door.

'They won't open the door', said the younger man, in a
voice of peculiar charm. 'They have been so frightened by the
fugitives and deserters roaming about the countryside after
this terrible war.' 'But where can we go?' said his companion.
'They *must* open the door to us. Why, it's Christmas Eve! I'll
say, "For Christ's sake", then we'll see how much that Name
still counts.' The younger man lifted his hand in gentle pro-
test, and then let it fall again, saying sadly: 'Too many bad,
cruel things have been done under cover of that Name! How
can a poor farm-hand know what to think?' But the older
man stood still at the door and knocked again, more loudly
than before. No one answered. Within the house silence
reigned. But the old man would not give in. 'Hello there!' he
called out: 'Please open the door . . . we are two travellers
who have lost their way. . . . Don't be afraid! Open to us in
the Name of Jesus Christ . . . we are freezing with cold.'

Suddenly a little window was opened in the stable close at
hand, and a brawny farm-worker peered out into the darkness:
'There are only two of them', he called out to someone behind
him, 'and they seem to be unarmed.' Then he shouted through
the window: 'It's no use your knocking! We won't let you
in. We haven't anything to give away to tramps! We haven't
enough for ourselves.' The older man simply said quietly, 'For
Christ's sake! You'll be sorry later if you don't let us in.'
All the farm-hand said was: 'So you think you can threaten

us, do you?' Then they heard another voice say in a loud whisper: 'Set the dog on them!' They heard a door being opened, and some dogs barking fiercely, and one came panting and growling round the side of the house. The older man jumped out of his way. The younger man rose slowly to his feet, and the two travellers disappeared into the darkness. Strangely enough the dogs ceased barking and came back into the house. Suddenly the wind dropped, and a few stars appeared in the clear night-sky. The farmer listened. He was afraid to show any lights lest some fresh danger should threaten them from without. Suddenly he saw a bright flame shooting up into the sky; it seemed to be a little way off, near the edge of the forest. 'Fire!' he cried. 'The wretches must have set the barn on fire!' With a pitchfork in his hand he rushed out of the house and everyone else rushed out after him, the farm-men, the stable-hands and even his wife and children, all shouting or weeping and wailing as they ran. 'Set the dogs on them!' shouted the farmer, but the dogs seemed to have vanished. The angry farmer ran on ahead, all his fears forgotten in the desire to catch those 'wretched fellows' before they could escape. Suddenly, he stopped stock-still, holding his pitchfork. The rest of the people followed him, then they too stood still, transfixed by the sight that met their eyes. 'O Lord Jesus', exclaimed the farmer's wife, as she sank to her knees and made the sign of the Cross; and the children and all the men knelt down and did the same.

For this is what they saw:

In a slight hollow in the ground stood a fir tree about the height of a tall man. They all knew this tree, but now it was transformed: it was on fire, but it was not consumed. The bright flames rose to heaven, but did no harm to man or beast. There it stood in its beauty, green and lovely, for the snow had melted from its branches and the flames seemed to envelope it in a shining golden mantle. Near it, on the ground sat the two travellers, their faces lit up by the burning tree as they held out their hands to the warmth of the fire. For some distance round the tree the snow had melted, making a kind of magic circle: there the grass was green and little wild flowers were blooming as if it were springtime. Under the tree the air was warm and scented as though it were already almost May. The two farm dogs, who would usually have nothing to do with strangers, were lying on the grass by the two

travellers; one of them had laid his head in the lap of the younger man, who was caressing it gently. The travellers had thrown off their heavy cloaks and sat there in brightly coloured 'foreign' clothes. Their faces shone in the light of the burning tree, and all around them there shone a heavenly light.

Now everyone knew who they were. Even the farmer understood; he dropped his pitchfork to the ground and went forward rather slowly. Then he knelt down and said: 'Lord, please forgive me for not knowing You, and for refusing to welcome you to my house. But so often at night we have been plagued by these disbanded soldiers, who are ready to steal and attack innocent people.' His wife joined him and she prayed: 'Have mercy upon us, and forgive us, we pray thee.'

The younger traveller (whom they now recognized as Christ himself with his friend and disciple St Peter) rose to his feet. First of all he touched the heads of the children who were kneeling before him with their parents. Then he made a sign to them and to all the other people to get up and stand before him. He looked at them with great kindness: 'Come nearer to the tree', he said, 'and get warm.' Then he led the children right up to the tree. They gazed at it with delight and wonder; for in its branches there were little birds singing away untouched by the flames. Apples and nuts hung on the lower branches and here and there they saw roses blooming as though it were June! Under the tree were several queer little animals rather like squirrels and hares, and yet they were different; these little creatures waggled their ears at the children.

Then the Lord lifted up one small child after another and told each one to take some of the fruit on the tree 'to eat and take home'. At first they were rather frightened; but when they saw that the flames did not touch them—all they felt was a pleasant warm glow—they picked the fruit and went back to their parents.

The farmer and his wife and the other men and women belonging to the farmer's household were kneeling on the ground, warming themselves at the glow. After a long silence, full of peace, the farmer spoke: 'Oh Lord! what a comfort it is to know that you are still alive, and not dead, as we thought!' His wife was startled and tried to stop him from saying 'things like that', but the Lord stretched out his hands at them both.

'Dear ones,' he said: 'Where one human heart seeks me and is not hardened by the cares and troubles of this world, I am always there, for I am alive for evermore.'

'Lord', said the farmer, 'would you be so very kind and even now come back this night to stay with us?' 'No, thank you,' said the Lord. 'Tonight you are *my* guests. Come, eat and drink with me in my supper.' And he stretched out his hands and fed them with food from heaven. They all ate and drank and were satisfied, and their hearts were glad.

After a long silence the Lord rose to his feet, took up his cloak and St Peter did the same. 'Oh, don't leave us yet!' implored the farmer. 'It is enough for the present,' said the Lord; 'but keep me in your hearts. I must travel further this night, for there are still so many hard, cold hearts which need my warmth and light.' He blessed them all, and prepared to leave.

At the last moment St Peter signed to the farmer to come

aside and speak with him. 'Listen,' he said, 'if anyone else knocks at your door in the night, do be human and kind. Don't be so frightened that you treat all strangers as though they were devils.' 'But how can we know?' said the farmer. 'That's the whole point,' said St Peter. 'You can't ever be sure who it is that comes to your door and is chased away! And it doesn't always turn out so well as it has this time.'

A few minutes later, after the last farewells had been said, the two travellers disappeared into the night. Then the men and women and children turned round and looked at the tree. Very slowly, one after another, the flames went out. Once more they were enclosed in the deep darkness of the winter night. But above them the sky was clear and the stars were shining with great brilliance. Then they all trooped back to the farmhouse and talked and talked about all that had happened, and were full of wonder and joy. And they praised God for his goodness and sang many a joyful carol.

That is why, men say, that on Christmas Eve in northern lands you will see a Christmas tree in every house, decked with candles, apples and nuts. Under the tree are toys and flowers.

3 · *The Holy Night*

SELMA LAGERLÖF

A Story from Sweden for Children

Many years ago in a large house in Sweden there lived a small
boy named Olaf, with his father and mother, five brothers and
sisters, and their grandmother. The children loved their grandmother very much, and they were in and out of her large
pleasant room at all hours. She always had time for them. Best
of all, she was a very good story-teller.

Now one Christmas Eve Olaf and his grandmother were
alone in the house. The rest of the family had gone off in a
big sledge to church for Midnight Mass. Both were feeling a
little sad at being left behind. One was too young and the
other was too old to be out so late. Grandmother saw that Olaf
was feeling disappointed, so she said: 'Shall I tell you a story?'
Olaf cheered up at once, and said, 'Yes, please, Granny!' So
she began:

ONCE upon a time, in mid-winter, a man went out on
a dark night to borrow some live coals to kindle a
fire. He went from house to house and knocked at
each door: 'Please help me,' he said. 'My wife has just given
birth to a child and we have no fuel for a fire. I *must* make a
fire to warm her and the little one.' But it was late, and all
the people were asleep. No one replied.

The man walked on and on; soon he left the village behind
and came out into the open country. At last, a long way off,
he saw the gleam of a fire. He walked towards it, and saw that

the fire was alight in an open field. A lot of sheep were sleeping round the fire, and an old shepherd, wrapped in a thick cloak, sat on a rock and watched over the flock. As the young man came nearer he saw that three big dogs were asleep at the shepherd's feet. All three woke up when they heard him coming; they opened their great mouths as though they were going to bark, but there was not a sound. They looked angry and dashed at the man, but did him no harm. The shepherd seemed to be almost asleep, and all the sheep were fast asleep too. They lay so close together that the man wondered how he could reach the shepherd to speak to him. After a minute or two he decided to go forward and pick his way through as best he could. So, very gently, he managed to weave his way in and out among the sleeping animals, and not one moved or woke up.

When the man had almost reached the fire the shepherd looked up. He was an ill-tempered old man, unfriendly and stern with human-beings. The moment he saw the man coming towards him he picked up his heavy stick and threw it at him. But the stick whizzed past the man without touching him. The young father went right up to the cross old man and said: 'Good friend, please help me, and give me some coals from your fire! My wife has just given birth to a child, and we have no fuel for a fire. I must make a fire to warm her and the little one.'

At first the shepherd only stared, for he wanted to say 'No'. But when he saw that the dogs did not bite the man, and the sheep did not stir as he stepped over them, and that the stick would not strike him, he felt afraid. So he said in a gruff voice: 'Yes, take what you need!'

But he said it in a strange voice, for, he thought to himself, he can't pick up burning coals!

To his amazement the young man bent down and picked up the burning coals with his bare hands, and he was not burnt; he wrapped them in his cloak, and it wasn't even scorched; and he carried the coals as easily as if they were apples or nuts! He thanked the shepherd warmly, and was just moving away when the shepherd called him back: 'What kind of a night is this?' he said, 'when dogs don't bite, and the sheep are not frightened, and the stick did not strike you, and the fire does you no harm?'

The young father was eager to get back to his wife, but he stood still for a moment and said gravely: 'I can't tell you. You must see it for yourself! Good night, and many, many thanks.'

Now the shepherd was so bewildered by these happenings that he followed the man at a distance to see if he could discover his secret. He followed him through the sleeping village and out on to the other side, where he found that this couple had no hut; they were camping in a cave among the hills. And when the old shepherd saw the mother lying there with her little baby in her arms, something kind stirred in his hard heart. 'Oh! that innocent child must not freeze to death,' he thought, and he wanted to help. So he opened his leather knapsack and took out a soft white sheepskin and handed it to the father. 'Take it,' he said 'and wrap up the child or he will freeze to death.'

And the moment that his heart was melted with compassion his eyes were opened. He saw a great light round the three figures in the cave, and all around him, in the air and everywhere, were hosts of angels singing that this night was born the Saviour which is Christ the Lord. He was so happy that he fell down on his knees and thanked God.

Then Grandmother looked into Olaf's wondering eyes and added: 'This light is not made by lamps or candles; it does not depend upon the sun or the moon or the stars. It is given to those whose hearts are kind and loving. They alone can see the glory of God.'

4 · *Christmas Eve on the Mountain*

ADALBERT STIFTER

A Story from Austria for Children

MANY years ago, in a remote mountain valley, there
lived a man and his wife with their two children,
Konrad and Susanna. The father was a shoemaker.
Indeed he was *the* shoemaker for the whole district; for his
shoes were so strong and so well-made that people came from
far and near to the little village of Gschaid, whether they
wanted shoes for their children or heavy climbing boots for
the men. His wife came from the next village, Millsdorf, which
was much larger and more important. The people of the two
villages had very little to do with one another; for one thing,
there was no road over the mountain ridge between Gschaid
and Millsdorf, but only a rough cart-track and a footpath.
The shoemaker's wife was pretty and friendly and clever,
but the people of Gschaid always treated her as a 'foreigner',
because she came from Millsdorf. Her father never came to
see her after her marriage; but her mother often walked over
the hill and through the forest to see her and the children.
She always brought little gifts for the children, and she told
them stories; they loved her very much. As they grew older
their mother often took them over to Millsdorf for the day,
and when Konrad was nearly ten, and Sanna was six, the two
children sometimes walked over the hill to see their grand-
parents, all by themselves. But their grandmother always sent
them off early, to be sure that they got home before dark.

So one day—it was Christmas Eve—Konrad and Sanna were

delighted when their mother came into their bedroom very early and said, 'It's a lovely morning . . . the sky is very clear and the sun is rising. There's no frost and no snow on the ground. Would you like to go over to see Granny this morning, and take her your presents? You could do it easily, and get back here before dark, before we light up the Christmas tree.'

The children jumped up and down with delight. 'Oh, yes, let's go.' 'Well,' said their mother, 'get your clothes on quickly, run into the shop, and ask your father if you may go.' They dressed very quickly, and soon came running back into the kitchen: 'Yes, Mum, Father says he thinks the weather is going to keep fine, and we may go.'

After breakfast their mother gave them the little parcels for her father and mother. Some she put into a leather satchel which Konrad carried over his shoulder, and the smaller ones were stuffed into the pockets of their outdoor clothes. Well wrapped up, and with a final word about 'being back before dark', the children set out.

They soon left the narrow streets of the village behind, and were out on the meadows; then they crossed a bridge over a small stream, but there was only a trickle of water. 'Why isn't there any water, Konrad?' said Sanna. 'Because this stream comes down from the Snow Mountain; you know, the one we can see from our front garden; up there it's very cold and the water is frozen hard.' They skipped along in the sunshine and up the hill till they came into the forest. Here too the ground was dry but not frozen. Now and then they ran off the path and kicked the dry leaves and fir cones which lay on the ground. Then the path became steeper and they had to walk more slowly. When they reached the highest point on the ridge the ground was frozen hard.

'When shall we see the painted signpost?' asked Sanna. 'It should be round the next corner,' said Konrad, looking round, 'but I can't see it.' Suddenly Konrad stopped and said: 'Look, Sanna, here it is, but it has fallen down.' This old signpost was painted red; it had been there for a long time. It had been put up in memory of a man who had died on that spot many years before. And now it lay by the side of the path among dry grass and dead leaves. 'It doesn't matter,' said Konrad, 'for we know the way, and we shan't miss it on our way back.'

Then the path went down a steep slope, zig-zag among the pine trees. The children ran down the path laughing at each other and enjoying the fun of running so easily down hill. Presently the trees thinned out, till the children were out on the hillside, looking down at the village of Millsdorf, which seemed to lie at their feet. 'Look, Sanna,' said Konrad, 'there's Granny out in the garden.' They shouted and waved. She looked up and waved back. About fifteen minutes later they were at her door. 'Come in, my dears,' she said. 'I *am* pleased to see you.' They all went into the kitchen, and the children took off their outdoor clothes. Then they sat down and watched her rolling out pastry while they told her all the news and drank hot milk and ate chocolate biscuits. Then they went to see their grandfather in his office; he too was very glad to see them.

Presently Granny called out: 'Come and get ready for dinner. The days are very short now, and you must get home before dark. It's Christmas Eve!' They had a very good dinner, and afterwards Granny said: 'I'm afraid you must be off.' So she gave them some bread and buns in case they felt hungry on the walk back. Then she filled the leather satchel with Christmas presents, tied up in neat little parcels, and filled their pockets with all kinds of nice things: nuts and sweets, biscuits and a little bottle with a special brew of black coffee. 'Take great care of this,' she said, 'and tell your mother it's a real medicine. It's so strong that a mere sip will keep a person from freezing, even on the coldest winter day.' Konrad thought it did not sound very nice, but he was too polite to say so. Then they said 'Good-bye! Happy Christmas!' and set out in good time to walk home.

They climbed the steep hill quite quickly; before they went into the forest they turned and looked down and waved, for Granny was at her door, waving a red handkerchief. Then they went on into the forest. It was much colder now and the sky was not so bright. They trudged on quite happily. Suddenly Konrad exclaimed: 'Look, Sanna! It's snowing.' At first only a few flakes floated down very lazily, like white butterflies. Sanna tried to catch them but they melted at once. Then the snow began to fall more steadily, and the children were delighted: 'It will be a real Christmas after all!'

When they reached the top of the ridge, Konrad looked round for the painted signpost, but he could not see it. Both children searched the clearing, but by this time the snow had covered everything. 'I expect we haven't got there yet,' said Konrad. So on they went, stopping now and then to look for the signpost, but by this time the snow was deeper, and they could not see anything. 'It must be further on,' said Konrad. It was very quiet in the forest. And all the time the snow was falling silently, covering the ground more and more deeply. They tramped on again, then Konrad said: 'Sanna, let's stand quite still, perhaps we shall hear something.' So they stood still; there was not a sound. 'Never mind, Sanna,' said Konrad. 'It's all right, just follow me and I'll get you home, don't be afraid.' Sanna was not afraid: she knew that Konrad would find the way. So she tramped on resolutely behind him in the snow.

Presently, to their surprise, they came to some rocks which towered above them like a great wall. 'Sanna,' said Konrad, 'we must be higher up than I thought! We must go on till we find a way that leads down hill; then it will be all right.' 'Yes, Konrad,' said Sanna. The children threaded their way in and out among the great rocks; up and up they went, the ground becoming steeper and steeper, and they had to walk more slowly. Whenever they stood still for a moment there was a great stillness, and everything was white. But the snow was dry, and they kept on shaking it off, so their clothes did not get wet.

At last they left the rocks behind; they tramped on and on through thick snow till they saw some strange objects ahead: 'What are they, Konrad?' asked Sanna. 'I don't know,' said Konrad, 'they look like the ruins of a big castle, but there's no castle up here.' When they came a little nearer, he said: 'Sanna, I know where we are. We're near the top of the Snow Mountain. These are great rocky peaks covered with snow. I've seen them in summer when there's no snow, and they look like great horns sticking up into the sky.'

They walked on a little further. Then Konrad stopped again and said, 'Sanna, these peaks aren't rocks at all! They're great blocks of ice. We're on the edge of the glacier!' 'What's a glacier?' asked Sanna. 'A river of ice,' said Konrad, rather absently, for he was looking about and wondering which way to turn. In all his life, even in summer, he had never been so high up, nor so far from home. So they clambered about in this wilderness of ice. Often they fell down, but they got up and went on. Suddenly Konrad noticed that the ground was less slippery and bumpy. 'Look, Sanna,' he said, 'here are some more big rocks. That means we're near the edge of the glacier, and we can get off the ice.'

It was easier walking, now, though their feet sank into the snow at every step. The daylight was fading, and Sanna was getting very tired. She began to cry. 'Don't cry, Sanna!' said Konrad, holding her hand. 'Look, here's a shelter for us.' They went under some overhanging rocks and found a kind of cave. Here the ground was dry, and free from snow. Snow and ice had filled up all the cracks, and it was almost warm. 'This will do splendidly,' said Konrad. 'It's getting dark, and we can spend the night here.' Sanna cheered up, and the children explored the cave. Sanna said that it looked just like a house. 'If we feel too cold in the night,' said Konrad, 'we must get up and walk about and clap our hands. Above all we must *not* go to sleep.' 'No, Konrad,' said Sanna in a sleepy voice. The children now realized that they were very hungry, so they took out the bread and buns which Granny had put in their pockets for the walk home. When they had eaten this they were still hungry. But Konrad said that it would be better to wait a little while before they opened the other packets to see what was in them. Then he took Sanna to the entrance of the

C

cave and helped her to shake the snow off her clothes and did the same for himself. Then he felt her hands; they were very cold. So he took off his jacket and wrapped it round her.

They sat still for a little while till it was quite dark, then they got up and went to the entrance. The snow had stopped. They peered out and looked up into the sky: it was now quite clear, and full of stars. 'It's Christmas Eve,' said Konrad, 'and all the houses in the village will be lit up. I wonder if we can see them.' They went a few steps outside the cave and looked out into the distance, but there was nothing but snow below and the stars above.

So they went back and sat down close to one another. 'Sleepy, Sanna?' asked Konrad, but she did not reply. Then Konrad shook her. 'Sanna! You mustn't go to sleep! Don't you know that?' 'Yes,' she murmured sleepily, but the next minute her head fell against his shoulder. Konrad sat and thought, 'Whatever shall I do? She must keep awake.' Then he remembered the bottle of black coffee which Granny had given him for their mother. '*She* won't mind,' he said to himself. He rummaged about in his satchel till he found the little flask. He unwrapped it carefully, and with a great effort he managed to draw the cork. Then he shook Sanna gently: 'Wake up, Sanna!' he said. 'I've got something good for you.' It was not easy to rouse her, but at last she sat up and said: 'What is it?' 'Look, it's the flask of coffee that Granny gave us.' Sanna drank a little. 'It's very bitter,' she said, 'but it's good, I feel much warmer.' Konrad drank some, too. Soon both children were wide awake, and warm right down to their toes. 'Granny did say it was a kind of medicine,' said Konrad, and they laughed. Then Konrad opened some of the other parcels, and he found sweet biscuits and ginger nuts and cheese biscuits and they had a good supper. After that they felt much better, and talked quietly to each other about all kinds of things. Now and again they took a little sip from the flask and each time they felt warmer and more wide awake.

Hours passed, and now and again Konrad wondered whether they would soon hear the Christmas bells from the valley. He would go to the entrance to the cave and listen, but each time it was the same. Everything was quiet . . . not a sound reached them. At last he began to feel tired and sleepy, and he looked at Sanna: she was already half-asleep. He roused himself, for he knew that this dozing was very dangerous. He opened the little flask, roused Sanna, and both children drank the last drops of coffee. For a little while they felt warmer and less sleepy, but this did not last long. Indeed, they were both on the verge of dropping off to sleep when suddenly they were startled by a very loud noise, close to them.

They sat up. 'What's that?' said Sanna. Konrad listened intently: then came two more sharp, loud cracking sounds. 'I know what it is,' said Konrad. 'It's the ice cracking in the glacier!' The noise was so alarming that they were now wide awake and all desire for sleep had gone. They got up, moved about, and kept looking out of the door of the cave.

At first it was all very still. All that they saw were the stars shining in the clear night sky. Then, without warning, something wonderful happened. As they stood near the entrance and looked out, a soft radiance began to shimmer behind the stars. Then it seemed to spread across the sky like an arch of silver. The silver melted into the palest green, and the arch grew brighter and brighter till it eclipsed the light of the stars. The children stood quite still, entranced by the beauty of the sight. As they watched, it seemed as though the radiance were moving, flowing in and out among the stars, while the arch itself blazed with a crown of light, in all the colours of the rainbow. The whole sky blazed with light and colour. Then, very gradually, the streams of light became paler and paler, till at last they faded away; once more there was nothing to see but thousands of stars in the dark sky.

The children were so delighted and astonished at what they had seen that they had no desire to sleep. Never before had they seen anything so lovely and so wonderful. After they had talked about it for some time they began to wonder what would happen next. They were just beginning to wish this night would end, when they saw that it was getting lighter.

The stars grew fainter . . . then a golden light began to gleam in the East.

'Sanna,' said Konrad, 'it's the dawn.' 'Yes, Konrad,' said Sanna. 'Can we go soon?' 'As soon as it's a little lighter we'll go outside, and then we'll *run* downhill to the valley!' said Konrad.

So they tidied themselves as well as they could, and ate a few biscuits. Konrad put some sweets in his pockets. 'Now let's go,' said Konrad, and they stepped out of the dark cave into bright sunshine.

At first they wandered about among the rocks, and up to the edge of the glacier. At last they came to a point where they could see no way forward, for they were at the top of a great cliff. So they turned back and tramped along in another direction till at last . . . at last . . . Konrad found a snow-field which went down hill. Slowly and carefully they began the descent. The snow was hard and the air was very cold, but the sun was shining and the sky was blue. They did not know where they were, but they were sure they would find the way home.

They had gone some way down hill when suddenly Konrad stood still: shading his eyes with his hand he said: 'Sanna, do you see something moving over there? . . . it keeps bobbing up and down.' 'Yes, Konrad, and it's red, it looks like a fire.' The children stood still and watched. The 'fire' seemed to be coming nearer; then it grew larger and they saw it more clearly. Still it came and went and they kept waiting for it to reappear over the snow. And as they watched, they heard, very far off, the sound of a horn. The children shouted as loud as they could, again and again, and then they heard the sound of the horn, a little louder this time. Again the children shouted and shouted, as loudly as they could, and after a few minutes they heard the horn once more; then they saw the 'fire' coming nearer, though it was still a long way off. And then they saw that it was not a fire at all but a scarlet flag, waving about as it was carried along.

Konrad said, 'Sanna, I know that flag! This means the people from our village have come to look for us.' Some moments

later he said: 'Yes, look! Those black spots in the snow are
people from our village. Look! That's Philip the shepherd.' A
little later the shepherd caught sight of the children. 'God
be praised,' he shouted, 'they're here!' He came up to the
children. 'So there you are! . . . The whole mountain is full
of people searching for you.' Then he turned to one of the men
who was with him and said: 'Go down at once to the Alp Hut
and ring the bell; then everyone will know that the children
have been found.' One man went off and told the news; they
all turned back and went on to spread the good news. Philip
and his companion took care of the children, helping them
through the snow and round the rocks. It was a long, steep
descent: sometimes the way was so difficult that the men
carried the children on their backs. Then, as they came nearer
the hut, they heard the sound of a bell. 'That's the bell from
the Alp Hut,' said Philip. 'That's to tell everybody that you are
both safe and sound. Now they know you're coming.'

Down another steep and slippery slope they went, and
there was their mother standing in the doorway of the hut.
She ran out to meet them. She was so overcome that for a
moment she could not say anything. They clung to her and she
hugged them. Then all three were in the Hut. 'Now, my
darlings, are you hurt?' 'No,' they said, 'not a bit.' But she felt
them all over and when she was sure that they were only cold
and hungry and very tired she gave them some hot soup and
tucked them up in the warm bunks. They snuggled down in
the blankets and dropped off to sleep. All the neighbours had
gone outside to leave the mother and children alone. When
Konrad and Sanna woke up they felt much better, but a little
confused. There were so many people about. Then their
mother said: 'Come to the door and look out,' and they saw
a number of men climbing up the hill, and all the time the bell
was ringing loudly over the snow.

One man was ahead of the rest. It was their father. His
wife called out, 'Sebastian! Here they are.' He went quite
white, trembled a little, and then ran to the children, took
them up in his arms, and for a few moments he could not

speak. Then he turned to his wife and exclaimed : 'Oh, Sanna,
Sanna!' He pulled himself together, picked up his hat, which
had fallen onto the snow, and went to the men who had been
helping in the search for the children; he stood still, struggled
to say something, but all he could say was: 'Neighbours,
friends! Thank you . . .'

Then he looked round and said in a quite ordinary voice,
'Well, since we are all here, let's go home.' So they all began
getting ready to go.

The Alp Hut was not very far from the village, but it was
high up. It stood on a ridge which ended in a rocky cliff; it
was so difficult to climb, that it was only scaled by rock
climbers in the summer; in winter no one could climb it at all.
So the whole party had to go back across the hillside, into the
forest, and then down by the cart-track into the valley. As
they were making their way slowly across the meadow near
the hut there floated up to them the sound of a bell. It was the
Sanctus bell. The Christmas Mass was being celebrated in the
village church. With one accord they all knelt down in the
snow, silently, and prayed. Then they got up again and went
on. Presently they heard voices and then they saw a group of
men straggling out of the forest in twos and threes; they were
men from Millsdorf who had also been out searching for the
children. Their leader was the children's grandfather. His face
was grey with fatigue and anxiety. He could hardly believe
his eyes when he saw Sanna in her father's arms and Konrad
walking cheerfully by his mother's side. 'God be praised,' he
called out to his son-in-law, 'but whatever happened?' 'They
were lost on the top of the mountain, and they even wandered
about on the glacier . . . they didn't know where they were,'
he shouted back. The grandfather joined the other group and
walked with his son-in-law. He listened to what he could tell
him, and then he said: 'We must thank God with all our
hearts that there was no wind. This is the heaviest snowfall in
this valley in living memory. If there had been a wind we
would never have seen the children alive again.' 'Indeed we do
thank God,' said the shoemaker, and both men were silent.

By this time the whole company had reached the valley. There, at the bottom of the hill stood a sledge, sent to pick up the children and their mother. Warmly wrapped in rugs and furs they were driven home. The men followed more slowly on foot. When the children reached home there was Grandmother standing on the doorstep to greet them. By the time the children had undressed and had eaten some food, they were quite dazed with fatigue and excitement. So their mother took them into their bedroom and in a few minutes they were tucked up and asleep. But she sat by Sanna's bedside.

After a time Sanna woke up and found her mother was holding her hand and stroking her forehead. Sanna began to talk. She told her mother a great deal about the day and night on the mountain. Then she added: 'When we were sitting in the cave up there on the mountain, d'you know, Mummy, I nearly went to sleep but not quite. . . . When I was very sleepy I saw a light and I saw the Christ-Child.' After a moment Mother said, 'I'm sure you did, my darling! He was with you in the darkness, and now he has left you some presents! D'you want to see them?' 'Oh, yes,' cried Sanna. She looked across to her brother and called out: 'Konrad, wake up! We're going to have our presents.' Very soon the children were up and dressed. Then mother opened the door between the two rooms and there stood the Christmas tree, covered with lights. A number of visitors came quietly into the room, and they all sang carols together.

This story about the Christmas Eve on the Mountain was never forgotten in the two villages. But the best of all was this: the children and their mother were no longer 'foreigners' in their own village. They now belonged. And after that the people of both villages became much more friendly; for they had worked together to find the two children on Christmas Eve.

5 · *The Avalanche*

HANNE MENKEN

A Story from Germany for Children

RUTH woke up with a start. Her bed was under the attic window, so she looked out to see what the day was like. But it was still quite dark. 'Not time to get up,' she murmured sleepily, and in another moment she was sound asleep once more. Suddenly—it seemed only a few minutes later—she heard a voice saying, 'Ruth, wake up!' Her grandmother was bending over her, with a kind smile on her face. The two other children woke up too. Grandmother said, 'Get up, quickly, my dears, it's Christmas Eve!' Ruth got up at once; Lena was still very sleepy, and little Peter stood up in his cot shouting, 'Christmas, Christmas! I want a drum, a drum', and he banged on the wall with his fists. Ruth went over to him and persuaded him to get out of bed. Then she helped him to get washed and dressed. When they were all ready they climbed down the ladder into the kitchen, where Grandmother was putting their breakfast on the table. They had steaming hot porridge and hot milk. Grandmother finished before they did, so she went outside to feed the goats and their one precious pig. When she came back, she said, 'Ruth dear, will you clear away and tidy up? I must get off at once.' 'Why are you in such a hurry, Granny?' said Lena. 'Because I want to get down to the market to help your father to sell his Christmas trees. He went out hours ago, and I promised to come as soon as everything was in order up here.' She bustled round the room to see whether she had forgotten anything; then she made up the fire in the big stove. 'That will keep you warm till this evening', she said. 'You needn't touch it again.' She put on her cloak, wrapped up her head and shoulders in a thick shawl and went off. 'Be good, my darlings,' she said, 'I'll be back before dark.'

When she had gone it seemed very quiet in the little house, which stood by itself high up on the side of the mountain, on the edge of the forest. The children were missing their mother very badly; she was ill in hospital down in the town below. Ruth played games with the children, told them stories, and they looked at picture books, but as the morning wore on they got very restless; Peter was noisy and Lena was fretful. Ruth was beginning to wonder however they would get through this long day indoors. Suddenly there was a knock at the door. Ruth opened the door and there stood a neighbour, who had come some distance through the woods to bring a Christmas gift for their mother. She left a large covered basket on the table: 'I expect one or other of you will be going down to see your mother? Give her this from us all, with our good wishes for her recovery.' She was gone before they could ask her any questions. At first Ruth said: 'We mustn't look into the basket, it's for mother.' But Peter and Lena were bursting with curiosity. 'Can't we see what's in it?' 'All right,' said Ruth, 'but don't touch!' She lifted the lid and they all peered inside, 'Oh, what a lovely cake!' It was covered with sugar icing. 'Yes', said Lena who had looked further down, 'and there are some fine red apples.' 'Mother *will* be pleased', said

Ruth, and for a little while the children chattered away about this wonderful present.

Suddenly Lena stopped chattering: 'But, Ruth, how shall we get the cake to her? If we leave it here too long it will get stale, and the sugar will get soft and sticky!'

Then Lena and Peter began to fidget. 'Tell us a story, Ruth', they asked. So she began, 'Once upon a time . . .' They were listening with great interest when suddenly the door opened, bringing a rush of cold air into the room. 'Good morning to you all', said the postman. 'Ah, you're all alone? Well, here's a postcard from your mother. Happy Christmas!' and he went off again on his long round. Ruth picked up the postcard and looked at it. On the top some words were printed: 'County Hospital', and on the other side there was a picture of the hospital. The children pored over this: 'Look,' said Lena, 'here's the door where you go in.' Suddenly Peter said, 'Can we go there, Ruth, now?'

For a moment the two girls gazed at him in amazement. Then they burst out laughing. 'Why, Peter, what a good idea, let's go this very minute!' 'Wait a minute', said Ruth, and she made them sit down and talk it over. They soon agreed that it would be a great pleasure for their mother, and they could easily walk there and back before Granny got home!

So they put on all their warmest clothes. Ruth picked up the basket, and carried it on her arm. Once she looked back at the little house: it looked so comfortable standing there in the sunshine; blue smoke was coming out of the chimney and the windows were so clean that they sparkled in the sunshine. The three children knew the way quite well; they walked in single file along the narrow footpath which had been cleared in the deep snow. As they went down the steep path the air seemed to be warmer. Some clouds gathered in the sky, the wind rose and blew the snow off the tips of the fir trees. But it was a curious kind of wind; it made them feel tired and sleepy. 'It's the *Föhn*,' said Ruth to herself, 'it always makes us feel queer.'

It was very quiet in the forest; the snow had become soft

and slippery, and little Peter began to cry: he was very tired. So they all sat down in the wet snow. Ruth opened the basket. 'There, Peter, lick a little of the sugar off the top of the cake, you'll soon feel better. Mother won't mind.' Peter took a good lick. 'That's good', he said, and in a few minutes he cheered up, and they went on down hill, towards the valley.

Suddenly the stillness was broken by a loud cracking sound. They stood still and listened. But everything was quiet again. Ruth said cheerfully, 'I expect they were working at the quarry some miles away. It's all right.' So they went on again and chattered away about Christmas Eve and the presents they hoped to get; Peter wanted a drum, and kept on talking about it. Then they left the footpath and came out on to the main road which ran through the valley. They had not walked far when a sledge overtook them. The driver pulled up and called out, 'Would you three like a lift?' Thankfully they climbed into the sledge; the farmer wrapped them up in his rugs, and off they went at a spanking pace. Peter was so tired that he leant up against Ruth and fell asleep.

A little later they reached the town, with its old houses and narrow streets. Their driver stopped in a wide open space round a large church. Here was the Christmas Fair, with its stalls and lights and crowds of people. Peter woke up. The children got out, thanked the farmer very nicely for the lift, and wandered out into the Fair. They were confused and bewildered by the masses of people, the shouts and cries and the numbers of pretty toys and ornaments and cakes on the different stalls. But the basket was very heavy, and they kept on bumping into people as they wandered about. Ruth soon realized that they had better go to the hospital at once, without waiting any longer. She asked the way and soon found the big ugly building which stood in a large square not far from the market-place.

They rang the large bell and Ruth asked to be allowed to come in and see their mother. At first the porter refused to let them in: 'We don't allow children to come in without grown-up people.' Ruth explained their plight, and then she added,

'We want to bring her a Christmas greeting'. 'Oh, all right', said the man, rather unwillingly. 'In you go! Ward 21, 3rd Floor; but mind you go quietly, you mustn't make any noise.'

They climbed the wide staircase, which was larger than anything they had ever seen before, and they sniffed as they climbed. 'What a funny smell', said Peter, wrinkling up his little nose. By the time they reached the 2nd Floor they stopped to rest. 'I must make you look a bit tidier', Ruth said to little Peter. She took out her handkerchief and tried to wipe his face. Peter didn't like this at all, and he got into a tantrum. 'I don't want to be clean', he shouted. 'Oh, do be quiet!' said Ruth, feeling at her wits' end. Peter was still being very difficult until she said: 'If I let you have another lick at the cake will you let me clean you up?' He calmed down at once, sat on the nearest step and licked rather hard, two or three times. But alas! the cake looked the worse for wear!

They heard steps on the stairs. The children stood still on the landing. A rosy-cheeked young nurse came up: 'Where do you want to go?' she asked. She told them exactly what to do and they soon found themselves standing outside Ward 21, 3rd Floor. Feeling very shy the children pushed through the doors and stepped into the ward. They saw a lot of people in bed all looking at them. Suddenly they heard a voice: 'Oh, my children!' They looked round and there in a white bed at the end of the ward lay their mother. They rushed to her. 'Oh, Mummy! Oh, Mummy!' said little Peter; and all three were in their mother's arms.

After they had talked and hugged to their hearts' content Ruth turned to the basket and opened it. Mother was delighted with it. 'We must cut it up in big pieces at once,' she said, 'for you children have had no dinner.' Then she looked at it rather carefully: 'Did it fall into the snow?' she asked, for she saw several damp patches where the icing had disappeared. 'No,' said Ruth, 'only I had to let Peter have a lick now and then.'

The children ate their cake with great gusto for they really were hungry. Then their mother became a little anxious: 'What will Granny say is she comes back and finds that you three have disappeared?' 'She's not coming back till evening', said Ruth. 'Still, it's past noon,' said their mother, 'and the sun sets very early at this time of year. Really, children, I think you should start out for home at once. Don't loiter by the way; be sure to get back before dark.' So they said good-bye, and promised to go straight home as soon as possible. 'And tell Father all about it this evening, and say I'm looking forward to his visit tomorrow. He'll tell me that you got back safely in good time.' So they kissed her once more, and when they reached the door of the ward they turned round and waved to her before the doors closed behind them.

Soon they found their way back to the Fair. They were so entranced with all the beautiful and funny things that they lingered for some time. Then they came upon a crowd of children looking up at something in the street: it was a Punch and Judy show. They had never seen anything like this before. They forgot all about their promises to their mother. Suddenly they felt rather cold, and there were men shouting out: 'The market is closed.' The three children came out of their dream. 'Oh, dear,' said Ruth, 'look! the sun has gone down behind the high mountains. We must get on as quickly as we can.'

They set out at a good pace, but no kind farmer met them with a sledge. It was hard going on the road which was very slippery. At last when it was nearly dark they reached the footpath which led uphill to their home. Up and up they climbed. At last Peter was so tired he had to sit down for a few minutes before he could go on. When they set out again Ruth began telling them stories and they walked more quickly and forgot their fatigue. Then they had to sit down again, and as they rested they looked up at the sky above them, and there shone the evening star. This made them think about the story of the Star, and of Christmas. Lena and Peter did not remember it very well, so Ruth told them about the inn and the shepherds and the Wise Men, and the Star, and as they climbed they sang verse after verse from the carols which they could remember.

They were not a bit afraid in the dark forest; the stars were shining overhead and they knew they would soon be home again and Granny would have supper waiting for them, and Father would be there, and they would tell him all about their visit to the hospital, and all that mother had said. Presently they came to a clearing in the forest and they were standing still for a moment to look up at the starlit sky when suddenly there was a sound of thunder. It seemed to come from a distance, and the sound echoed from one side of the valley to the other. Then all was still.

The three children clung to one another. 'It's an avalanche!' said Ruth, in a rather small voice. 'Perhaps over there, on the other side of the valley. Come, let's get home quickly!'

They went further up the hill and they thought they heard voices. When they came to the next clearing, where several paths met, the whole forest seemed full of people. They were all running uphill calling out to each other: 'An avalanche!' The three children were caught up in the crowd. No one noticed them. When they came out on to the open ground before their house there was such a crowd that the children could not see the house at all, and they could not get through the crowd. Most of the people were very quiet. Then some men called out for picks and shovels and others answered them. Then they heard people talking quietly to one another. Ruth listened to a woman standing near her. She was talking to a friend: 'There isn't much hope,' she said. 'The avalanche has crushed the roof as if it were made of paper!' She said no more. The only sound was the hammering of the men who were trying to get into the little house. 'One of the goats is dead,' said the woman, 'but the other is alive. The three children were alone in the house, they can't be alive. Their grandmother is heartbroken. See! There she is, sitting on that treestump over there.'

Peter and Lena were crying with fatigue and bewilderment, but Ruth had grasped what had happened. She pushed hard through the crowd, pulling the children after her. Then she saw the ruined house. 'Grandmother', she called out—but no one heard her. Torches lit up the scene of desolation. Grand-

mother was crying bitterly. 'Grandmother!' Ruth called out
again, as loudly as she could. The three children ran across
the open space and the bewildered grandmother saw her three
grandchildren standing before her safe and sound. She hugged
them, and they clung to her. The men laid down their axes in
astonishment, and one of them was their father. For a few
moments there was a great stillness. . . . Then the neighbours
cried out: 'God be praised', and some of the people cheered.

After a meal with a neighbour the children were carried
downhill to the main road. There stood a sledge, waiting for
them. They bundled in and were driven to their grandmother's
house in the town. As they got out of the sledge, they saw
that the house was brightly lit. When they got inside there
was the mayor of the town and the priest and a number of
friends who welcomed them back. The mayor said to the
children's father: 'Don't worry, we'll see you get another
house, and you won't have to pay anything for it!' Then they
all went into Granny's sitting-room and there stood the tree,
blazing with lights. The room was full of friends and relations.
Then they offered a prayer of thanksgiving, and they all sang
carol after carol, joining hands round the tree. Then came the
presents. Somehow each child got what he or she most wanted;
above all, Peter had his drum!

Late that night, when the lights on the Christmas tree had
gone out, and the guests had gone, and the children were in
bed, their father and their grandmother went up to see if the
children were asleep. There they lay, peaceful and unharmed.
'Oh, Mother', said the man, deeply moved. 'Truly God sent his
angel this night. This is the most wonderful Christmas I've
ever known.'

6 · The Christmas Mail

A. DE MECK

A Story from Norway for Children

FATHER was a postman. It was delightful, Ola thought, to have a father who was a postman, especially such a brave and gallant father as his father was. For it was no joke being a postman in this district. It was not a question of walking around well-paved streets, delivering letters in a row of beautiful houses. In the summer it was all right, cycling or walking the many miles between the farms with the post he had fetched from the railway station down below in the valley, but in winter, when their strong little horse had to fight his way through the blizzard; or, even worse, when the snow was so high that father had to put his skis on, leave the horse in some farm, and carry the post on his back to the most remote farms, it was a very hard job indeed!

Tomorrow was the greatest day of all the year; it was Christmas Eve. Everybody expected the postman then. There would be parcels coming to most people, or Christmas greetings and cards. How Ola wished he was grown up, and not only twelve, and could be a postman like his father! Meanwhile, he had his little job to do. It was Christmas Eve tomorrow, and he had gone out into the forest to cut the Christmas tree. They were all busy now at home. The smoked sausages and the smoked ham were hanging from the rafters, the Christmas cakes were in their boxes, nice little doughnut sort of cakes, and small round dry ones, with sugar and almonds on the top. They did not taste too bad either, he thought, for his sister Marit had given him a couple of broken ones this morning when she was putting them away in the boxes. They only had three kinds of pastries with the Christmas fruit cake that mother would make tomorrow. In other places they had more, and in the large, rich farms down in the valley they made as many as seven kinds. But then, of course, his home, Firhill, was only a small place. It had climbed far up the hill-side, and lay there, small and grey, nestling in the forest. They had only two cows, and of course their darling Blackie, the postman's gallant little horse.

It was lovely standing there, just being happy, looking forward to Christmas, hoping that father and mother had remembered what he had told them once, that he wished he had a nice big knife in a leather sheath. How lovely it was all around him; the snow lay heavily on the branches of the trees, glittering like diamonds in the golden light of the afternoon sun. 'And now for the Christmas tree,' thought Ola. He selected a nice round even one, about as tall as himself, with firm, well-shaped branches, shook the snow from it and chopped it carefully off. He laid it on his little sledge, thinking all the while how lovely it would look dressed in all its glory of paper garlands, many coloured small baskets with sweets in them, red and blue candles, and at the top, the lovely glittering silver star that Marit had made yesterday out of chocolate paper. Humming softly to himself the tune of an old familiar Christmas hymn, he walked slowly homewards pulling his little sledge.

He had nearly reached home when he saw his sister Marit running breathlessly towards him. He looked at her face and knew that something was wrong. 'Ola, Ola, father has hurt himself, he has broken his leg, come quickly, Ola,' cried the girl. Ola felt a shiver go down his spine; the Christmas Mail! He suddenly realized that it was almost dark and bitterly cold. Marit, who had forgotten to put her coat on, stood shivering and crying by his side. 'Don't cry, old girl', he said as hand in hand they ran towards the house.

D

Ola was rather scared when he looked at his father lying in his bed with his bandaged leg. Mother looked a little scared too, he thought. As for his younger brother Finn, and his two little sisters, Kari and Elsa, they were for once absolutely silent. At the same time Ola had a funny sort of feeling inside, as if he were hoping for something . . . the Christmas Mail . . . would father ask . . . could he? 'Well, my boy,' said his father's voice, 'you'll have to do it; we cannot keep people waiting on Christmas Eve. The mail must get through!' Ola had a funny feeling as if the lamp danced on the table and the floor rocked. He was so proud to be the one to carry the mail. He drew himself up smartly, 'Yes, Father,' he said, 'I understand. The mail must get through!'

That night, after supper, he fixed the little Christmas tree on a little wooden foot, to make it stand. He sat there cutting the wood off to fit the foot, and all the time the same words rang through his head: 'The mail must get through, the mail must get through.' And it was he who had to do it. Could he do it?

He looked across the room at his mother, and she smiled back at him. 'I would go to bed if I were you, Ola, my child, I beg your pardon—my son, the postman,' she said. Was she laughing at him? No, perhaps not.

That night, when he said his prayers, he said all the usual ones he used to say every night, 'God bless and protect Father and Mother, Marit and Kari, and Elsa and Finn, and Uncle John and Aunt Anna in the town!' But, at the same time, one thing kept ringing in his head: 'Dear God, please let me bring the mail through!'

At four o'clock his mother called him. He was wide awake at once and jumped out of bed. This was his great day. He ate his hot porridge and went out. It was pitch dark. Great black clouds covered the sky, but the snow gave a kind of dim light, and besides he knew the way as well as he knew his own pocket. Blackie put his wet nose to his cheek, and the boy threw both his arms around the animal's neck and gave it a tight squeeze. 'We must get the mail through, mustn't we,

Blackie?' he whispered, and the faithful little horse pricked up his ears; he understood the situation fully.

Off they started at a brisk trot down the steep, uneven path. Both horse and driver knew every curve and every turning, and after some time, when they grew accustomed to the dark, they could make out the trees and bushes around them. It was like a fairy-tale ride. Boughs laden with snow swished past Ola's face. The trees looked like friendly giants, or 'trolls' as we call them in Norway. Trolls are generally bad, but Ola was not afraid of these, they seemed to wish him well. Blackie slowed down, the path had become more difficult, and dry, cold snow-flakes fluttered down from the heavy clouds. At last they were on the high road, and Blackie galloped joyously ahead. They passed houses where lights were beginning to show, and smoke curled up from the chimneys. It was nearing seven now, and the railway station was not far off.

'Good morning, Mr Olsen,' Ola called out, as he saw the station-master on the platform. 'Father has broken his leg, so I'll have to take the mail instead!' 'Good morning, lad, you'll have a tough job of it, if it keeps on snowing like this, but you'll manage it all right, sonny, if you hurry,' replied the kindly station-master, who was also the post-master. 'The mail will be ready in a quarter of an hour. Come and have a sandwich and a cup of coffee before you start.'

And now Ola and Blackie were on the road again, with their precious burden stowed safely away in the back of the sledge. There were thrilling-looking parcels of every shape and de-scription, letters and gaily coloured post-cards for nearly every-body in the place. How Ola looked forward to delivering them and giving pleasure to so many people! He felt a little as if he were Santa Claus himself.

When he came to the farms the children rushed out to meet him with cries of joy. 'This must be my skis coming from town', cried little Anders at the big white farm by the road-side, as Ola stopped before the gates holding out a long parcel in brown paper. 'Your skis; what nonsense you are talking! Santa Claus must know if you are a good boy until this evening before he brings you anything', said his mother, laughing as she quickly tucked the parcel under her apron. 'Thank you, Ola', she said to the boy. 'Here is a nice piece of cake for you, and a merry Christmas to you and your people', she added, as he drove off.

'And now for the little grey farm at the foot of the hill', thought Ola. He looked forward particularly to that, though he knew he would get no piece of cake there. They were very poor at that house, he knew, and Christmas would not be as bright there as most other places. But he had a registered letter for them, a big fat one, with foreign stamps. Their eldest son had gone to America, he knew, and perhaps this was a Christmas present from him! 'Hullo!' He stopped at the house and shouted 'Hullo!' as loudly as he could through the howling wind and the snow, but nobody heard. Evidently they had not heard Blackie's jingling bell either, for nobody came out. Ola jumped off with the letter in his hand and ran to the door and knocked. A pleasant woman, thin and tired-looking, opened the door, 'Hullo, Ola', she said kindly. 'Out in this weather? Come in and warm yourself, sonny!' 'Mrs Nordset,' shouted Ola excitedly, 'I have a letter for you, a registered letter!' Mrs Nordset signed her name and opened the letter like a person in a dream. 'It is from Einar', she said with a happy smile, 'and there is a lot of money in it.' 'Now we will be able to pay the rent and have a happy Christmas', said her husband who had come up behind her. The children who had stood awed and silent now began shouting and jumping. 'God bless our dear boy,' said the mother smiling, 'and thank you, Ola, and a merry Christmas to you!' 'A very happy Christmas to you all', Ola called out, disappearing in the storm, happy at heart, for it was a very wonderful thing to be able to bring joy and happiness wherever he went, even though through no merit of his own.

It was the same everywhere; he seemed to spread joy on his way. Some got unexpected presents, some got parcels they had been hoping for, others again got greetings and letters from friends and relatives far away, loving thoughts that cheered them and made them happy.

Ola by this time was thoroughly tired, cold and hungry. It had been a long morning and dark was not far off. It had been tiring, too. Once Blackie had stumbled and all the mail had fallen off into the road. He had spent a long time picking it up in the snowstorm, and making sure it was all there before he started off again. Another time they went off the road and into the wood, and had to go back a long way before they found the road again; indeed, they were lucky to find it at all. Blackie was very tired, too. His legs were sinking deep into the snow with every step as they picked their way carefully among the trees to the farm of Uncle Mons. There it was at last, he could see the light in the windows. He stumbled off and knocked at the door.

It was wonderful to come into the light, to be near the fire, to have something hot to drink and a nice dinner to eat, while Aunt Hanna was fussing round him, drying his wet jersey and his black and white woollen mittens, stiff with ice. Uncle Mons had gone out to give Blackie a sack of oats, and came back, saying: 'Blackie is worn out, and so are you, Ola boy, stay here tonight, and I will bring the rest of the mail round for you, how much is it—let me see—two parcels and seventeen letters.' But Ola was on his feet, 'Thank you very much, Uncle,' he said, 'but this job was entrusted to me, I must get the mail through!' 'A true son of your father! You'll make a fine postman soon, God bless you', smiled Uncle Mons, and once again Ola was out in the storm.

This time he was alone. Poor little tired Blackie was spending Christmas Eve in the warm stable in the company of Brownie, Uncle Mons' big brown horse. The parcels were heavy on Ola's shoulders, and his skis difficult to manage in the loose snow. But on he went from door to door with his gifts. The last he visited was old mother Elin, and for her he had a big heavy parcel from her married daughter in Oslo. And it was a gift indeed. Ola stood in the doorway watching her unpack it. First there came a large ham, then coffee, sugar, nuts, dates, chocolate and lovely decorated candles to place on the table. 'God bless you, Ola,' she cried, 'for bringing it in time. We would have had a meagre festival if you hadn't come tonight. Here is the biggest bar of chocolate for you, and a merry Christmas, sonny.' 'Merry Christmas, and thank you, Ola!' cried her three small grandchildren and danced round him. 'A merry Christmas to you all', Ola shouted back as he set off.

And now—home! There, up that hillside in the heavy snow.

Every step cost him an effort, tired as he was. And now, along that ridge . . . Mind, not too much to the left, for though you cannot see it in the blizzard, there is a sheer drop of several hundred feet . . . Now turn right . . . there is the little log bridge over the frozen stream . . . good. But where is the path up the hill-side, his hillside, where his home lies? It must be in this direction, he thought, and struck out through the snow-drifts. On and on he went, but no farm appeared between the trees. If he could only sit down and rest for a moment, but he knew he must never do that, it would mean certain death! Tired as he was, if he sat down he would fall asleep and freeze to death. His only chance of safety lay in fighting on through the pitiless lashing snow and the black night. He stopped for a second to get back his breath. If he sat down now—just for one minute . . . At that moment he heard a sound, somebody was calling his name through the howling wind: 'Ola, Ola!' and with one great cry of 'Mother!' he stumbled forward towards the voice.

Christmas Eve is a very important day in Norway, so

mother had of course a lot to do after Ola had left, and so had
everybody in the house. Marit had scrubbed and washed the
whole place clean. Mother baked the last pastries and buns,
while the small ones decorated the little tree. Father lay on a
couch and helped them. The day went slowly by, it began
to grow dark, and still Ola had not returned. At last all the
preparations were finished. Mother went to the stable, and
gave the cows an extra helping of hay. Kari called out, 'We
must not forget the sheaf for the birds!' Finn raced out to the
barn and came back with a large golden sheaf of corn, the last
one to be bound last autumn, and always kept till Christmas
for the little birds, who must have their winter feast as well as
the humans. It was fastened on a pole on the roof of the barn.
What a jolly time they all would have, the red-breasted robins,
the cheeky sparrows and all the others!

Marit had also finished. The last thing she did was to lay an
armful of fir-branches on the doorstep. Of course you did that
every Saturday, but on Christmas Eve you put an extra lot of
them and they smelt so wonderfully. How people in towns
could bear to have just dull, dead door-mats she never could
understand. Now all the children were marched off to the tub
with hot water, and even Finn did not object to having his
ears washed. After all, Christmas was only once a year!

Dressed in their best clothes they sat silently in the room,
for Ola had not yet come. All day they had been thinking of
him, wondering how he was getting on. Now they sat there in
the warm, cosy room listening to the wind howling in the
trees and the snow lashing like small white streaks against the
black panes. They were all anxious. It was late. What if he
had lost his way, what if something had happened to him! The
tree stood there ready. Father was lying on his couch with the
big Bible, ready to read the Christmas story. They all waited,
and each of them prayed in his heart: 'Dear God, let nothing
have happened to him.'

Suddenly, mother got up and opened the door. A cold blast
entered the room, making the candles flicker. She went out
through the front door and into the night. They heard her

call, 'Ola, Ola!' and then, after what seemed to them a very long time, a happy shout. 'Here he is!' And in she came with a wet and tired, but, oh so happy boy! And then it was a glorious Christmas Eve. Father read the wonderful story of the birth of our Lord, and with tears of joy in their eyes they all sang the beloved old hymn: 'Silent Night, Holy Night, all is bright!' How joyously the candles on the little tree twinkled, how lovely the presents looked lying at its foot, how they all listened when Ola told them his adventures! How happy they were to be reunited. For them *that* was the most wonderful present the Little Jesus had sent them on the Blessed Night when he was born.

7 · *Santa Risolina*

HEINRICH FEDERER

Many years ago a Swiss poet was on a walking-tour in Italy, in mid-winter. One day he set out to climb to the top of a neighbouring pass. On the way up he fell in with a delightful Italian couple: Ignazio and Laetizia. They too were making for the top of the pass, where they had to look after some animals who were grazing up there. Laetizia was very gay and sparkling; and she was a great talker. In the course of conversation something was said about 'the saints'. 'Oh', she exclaimed: 'I simply can't bear pictures of sad and gloomy saints. The one I like most of all', she went on, 'is the Beata Maria di Castelletto. I call her "Santa Risolina".' A little later on, the three travellers reached a point where there was a little shrine, dedicated to Santa Risolina, and a wooden bench for the use of the passersby. So they all sat down to rest. As they sat there Laetizia told the poet the story of the saint.

SIGNORINA Risola laughed a great deal, and no one ever laughed with more grace and charm. People used to say as they listened to her: 'You couldn't tell whether you were listening to the bells ringing in Rome, or whether the sun had begun to sing!' Everybody loved to hear her laughing, that is, everyone except sour-faced hypocrites. Ah well! It all happened fourteen hundred years ago . . . but believe it or not something very wonderful happened in those days. That was when someone *did* object to her laughter. The angels in heaven (at least a few of them) began to envy a young girl who was always happy, because however hard they tried they found they could not laugh with the same freedom and purity as the Signorina in Castelletto. So some of them got together and agreed that they 'must do something about it'. They waited till Christmas was near, when, as everyone knows, the Christ-Child comes down to earth in great poverty and humility. They said to each other: 'Is it fitting that *he* should put up with all this, and all the time that Maria di Castelletto goes on laughing? Whatever will people think? Down there, after all, it is a vale of tears. It's certainly no paradise. She ought not to be allowed to go on like this.' Some of them shook their heads and murmured 'It's a scandal!'

Finally, they went to the Christ-Child himself and told him all about it. He listened carefully; then he said: 'But what can you do about it? You can't stop that kind of laughter any more than you can prevent the sun from shining or water from flowing.' He seemed to be quite serious as he said this, but one of the angels noticed that his lips were quivering a little and that there seemed—for some reason—to be a light in his eyes! But the serious young angel thought no more about it. For he and his friends were so concerned about their own shocked feelings that they did not notice anything else. After a moment or two they said, very politely: 'Lord, may we make a suggestion? First of all, will you begin your visit to that region at Norcia? Then we will go down and visit the castle and see what we can do. Perhaps this foolish girl may be persuaded to receive you in a more fitting manner.'

So it was arranged. And towards Christmas four angels went down to earth and reached Castelletto. It is a little town in a valley among the mountains. When they reached the stone bridge over the foaming little river, they washed their hands and feet in the icy waters, in order that they might appear before this young lady looking very clean and cool!

When they came near the castle where the Signorina Marietta lived with her family and her large household of maids and serving men, the angels already heard the sound of her

melodious laughter. Now the youngest of the four angels had
been very fond of dancing when he lived on earth. Suddenly
he felt he could not go on with this visit. He made the Sign of
the Cross and slipped away.

At last the three other angels reached the gateway of the
castle : they looked through the great archway into a large
courtyard and they saw that it was full of happy faces and
lights and the sound of singing. On the further side of the
courtyard they saw the Signorina herself, surrounded by children, many of them cold and frightened. She was kneeling on
the stones amongst them, comforting them, and cheering them
up; finally she made them all laugh. In the end all these children ran into the ring with the other children and joined in
the singing-games. Old and young danced and sang together.
Then the three angels saw how the Signorina Marietta went
round amongst them, giving a present to each one, and all in
such a gay and charming way that even her smile was itself a
gift. Then the whole company broke out into singing and as
they sang they joined hands and danced, their faces shining
with joy.

Now the next-youngest angel (who had been Director of
Music at Perugia when he lived on earth), who thought he was
proof against all the dancing and skipping in the world, began
to tremble from top to toe. Then he sneezed and said, 'Excuse
me, brethren, I have forgotten my handkerchief . . .' and he
basely deserted them, and disappeared from sight. The two
angels who had held firmly to their resolution now realized
that they dare not approach this gay crowd in their celestial
costume. So they changed their snow-white feathers into beggars' rags; then they managed to cover their faces with a grey
veil which made them look miserable and forbidding. They
stepped through the archway into the very midst of this cheerful noisy crowd, marched straight up to Signorina Marietta and
held out their hands, and in a feigned voice they whined for
alms. She looked at them with astonishment, yet with a kind
and smiling face : 'Here you are', she said, and gave them some
delicious sweetmeats. The two angels (who now looked like

very old women) refused these gifts. 'Too sweet for the likes of us', they murmured, in a rasping voice. 'Nothing can ever be too sweet to be given or received,' added the Santa Risola, 'especially when the Christ-Child will be visiting us.' The two beggars stood there, silent and disapproving, so she added, 'Well, will you at least accept these furs to keep you warm? For I can see you are suffering from the cold; or would you rather have some sandals for your feet? They will make it easier to walk along the rough roads.'

'No,' they said. 'No, thank you, Signorina; we don't want anything of that sort!' Then she suggested several other gifts which would make their lives easier and pleasanter, but they refused them all. She stood there baffled, wondering what she could do for these strange old creatures. Then they hinted that they wanted a gift of another kind, and as they talked their voices sounded hoarse and rasping.

'What *can* I give you?' said Marietta, eager to hear what they really wanted. 'Your laughter,' blurted out the two angels, 'give us your laughter.'

'What on earth do you mean?' said the Signorina, as if she could not understand what they were saying. 'You are joking,' she added, 'that is quite clear!' And she began to sing, and then to laugh, and everyone stood and listened for her very laughter sounded like larks singing in springtime.

But the two angels took no notice: 'It's no joke, Signorina,' they said, 'far from it.' 'But why do you want my laughter? What do you want to do with it?'

'We want to pack it up properly, and seal it, and send it up to heaven. It would be far more suitable up there. Then it will be waiting for you there. When you enter the door into Paradise it will be given to you, and it will break out once more.' Then they looked at her severely, saying: 'You must excuse us for speaking so frankly, but really, in this vale of tears, and while there is still time for repentance, it is an extravagance . . . indeed, it is very shocking! Come, Signorina, give it to us, and then try to cry a little for a change.'

Marietta listened with growing amazement. She looked as

though the words she heard were incredible. For a few seconds she was silent with astonishment; then she threw back her head and pealed with laughter. She was so completely doubled up with laughter that everyone joined in. Many of the women had to sit down to recover, as they wiped their eyes and looked at the two miserable old women, who stood there, looking most awkward and embarrassed.

At last Risolina recovered and began to speak: 'I do believe that you must be two of those ancient sibyls who sit up there on the mountain top, turned to stone, and now you have made up your minds to come down to us at Christmas to show how poor you are. You poor heathens! Now I understand why you can't laugh. How can you when you feel like this? If only the Christ-Child were here, but he always goes to Norcia first of all, and then he comes on to us by way of Cerreto. He can turn your miserable faces into joyful ones with one look from his eyes. But I am only an ignorant girl—whatever can I do?' Then she turned to the children: 'Come children,' she cried, 'come to these poor creatures, take their hands and warm them, cheer them up. Some of you might play the pipes for a joyful Psalm, perhaps the eighth Psalm or the 33rd? And then we can all dance to a gay tune, and we'll beat time for you. Perhaps all this will help our friends a little.'

As you can imagine, the two angels were not at all pleased to be called 'heathens' and then to hear that they were to be pitied. And as the first sounds of the dance and the singing began to reach them, they tried to shut their eyes and ignore what was going on. Very soon this was impossible, for the children skipped round them laughing and singing; and some of them whispered funny things into their ears, and almost made them laugh. At last they gave up the attempt to ignore the gay life around them. They began to look, and to listen to the music (for, as you know, all the angels are musical and nearly everyone can play an instrument).

And the more they looked and listened the more interested they became: they wanted to hear whether the players kept good time, and whether they played with the right expression.

Then, without realizing it, they began to sway with their limbs and soon they were keeping time with the players. Marietta noticed this and she beat time with her graceful arms, and everyone sang and danced with greater delight than ever! And as the joyful Psalm about Jerusalem and her golden towers rose from a hundred children's voices and the children waved their arms towards heaven, it was all up—the two disguised angels could not hold out any longer. They rose to their feet, turned heavenwards and bowed their heads in worship, then they joined in the dance, and sang and sang, and at last even they began to laugh with the rest of the company. The whole assembly was amazed: they had never seen such dancing, so full of life and grace. But their amazement grew when, as the supposed 'beggars' joined in the festival, their very clothing began to change in form and colour. Finally all the old rags fell off and the snow-white feathers came through, showing the angels' lovely wings; and so, to their astonishment, everyone saw that these people were not ancient sibyls at all, but angels from heaven. And all danced together hand in hand; and as they danced they sang with the heavenly choir:

> Glory to God in the Highest
> and on earth peace, to men of goodwill.

The poet was so moved by this ancient legend that he almost felt the presence of the young Marietta. His young friends had gone on ahead. He sat on alone in the winter silence among the mountains, and sometimes it seemed to him as though there were sounds of distant laughter, but it was very quiet and far away. The valley, the little river, the rocks and the forests, and the vast expanse of mountain, sky and earth, seemed to be echoing this laughter, as though there were nothing in the whole world but peace and joy among all men.

8 · *Long Ago in Norway*

SIGRID UNDSET

HELGA, the grandmother at Uvaasen, came out of the little stall, put down her milk-pail in the snow, and looked up at the sky. But the sky was very grey and the clouds were heavy with snow. Snow covered the whole meadow like a winding sheet, so smooth that it had neither light nor shade. Its surface was so uniform that one could hardly detect any of the contours of the mountain-side. The line of the brook—which in summer flowed and purled so merrily through the meadow—was now merely a grey shadow in the snow. The marks of Signe's skis disappeared far below. The grandmother gazed in that direction : 'Signe must have reached the Hallsteins by now', she thought. From that point it was a two hours' walk to the church in the village.

The farm of Uvaasen lay on a gentle slope, on the mountain-side. The whole clearing was surrounded by forest, above and below. Looking towards the valley all one could see was the blue-black carpet of dark forest; looking uphill, there was a grand view of the snow-covered peaks with their granite cliffs, very white against the grey sky. A faint murmur of sound stirred among the forest trees and through its snow-coverlet one could hear a faint murmur of sound from the brook far below.

Then the grandmother looked back at the farm-house, with its large white cross, newly painted on the door. Then she picked up her pail, noticed that the warmth of the new milk had made a ring in the snow, and walked along the narrow path which had been cleared between the farm-house and the barn.

Both her little grand-daughters were standing outside, on the open space in front of the house, holding the keys of the store-room in their hands. Their grandmother had promised them that they might help her carry the big loaf and the Christmas Candle into the house. Before she left, their mother had dressed them in their Sunday clothes: they had new ribbons in their hair and new belts over their older winter frocks.

It was pitch-dark in the store-room; but the room was not very large and it was not so full that one could easily go wrong in the dark. Now and again as they groped for the food they wanted they bumped against bundles of dried fish. Although it was so dark in there, the children soon found the side of bacon and the frozen hare which had been saved for their special dinner next day. Audhild had to carry the Christmas Candle and the special Christmas bread, while her sister Inge was given the wheaten bread which Helga had received as a gift from the sister of the village priest, the last time that she was down in the village at the parish church.

When they went outside again it was already twilight. 'Already', they thought, 'the Christmas bells will be ringing in the valley.' The old woman stood on the step for a moment before going into the house: she remembered that it had been her husband's last job to clear this open space in front of the house in order to make the house itself more comfortable. He died about this time of year, when they had only been married for seven years. Then she recalled that on January 11th, it would be seven years since Haldor and Signe were married. Were they too to meet the same fate? Were two widows now going to sit here with three little children to care for and a fourth expected on the 15th of May? 'No, no!' she said in her heart: 'Signe must stay down there in the village at the rec-tory, and go to the parish church very often, where the priests sing and the lights on the altar are gleaming and the fragrance of incense fills the air! Then she will be safe and the evil spirits out there in the darkness will be kept at bay! For Mary's Son was born in Bethlehem, and the power of the evil spirits was broken by his coming.' Helga then lifted Inge up in her arms, and over the high step, and set her down safely in the house.

E

Before she left, Signe had tidied up the main room very thoroughly : she had put sweet-smelling resinous wood on the hearth, and she had placed a great candle on a wooden bench. 'People like us', she said, 'can't be bothered with a table.' Helga went through the room and bent over her son. He was lying there asleep. His wife had washed him and put on a clean shirt. But his face was ashen, and his hands lay limply on the cover-let, looking like wax. His mother made the sign of the cross over him and recited a brief prayer before she turned away to give the children something to eat. The little girls looked at her with great expectation as she cut the loaf into four parts. Then she broke one part into several pieces, threw them into the frying pan, lifted it off its hook, fried the pieces of bread in it, and then took the food and placed it on the wooden bench.

Arne, the youngest grandchild, stirred in his hammock cradle and cried out—the smell of the food had wakened him. Grandmother took him on her lap, fed him with little scraps of bread, and each time she hugged him a little closer to her breast.

Signe had borne beautiful children, and she looked after them and everything in the house very well indeed. And as Helga thought about her daughter-in-law, her heart warmed to her. Then she turned to the thought of Olav, who had left her, after he had lost his promised bride through a fatal illness. She was a girl to whom he had been betrothed from child-hood; after her death he could never feel at home in Uvaasen. Three years ago he had sent good wishes to his mother through a mutual friend, and once he had sent her a cloak by the hands of a servant of the Bishop of Hamar. At that time he was living in Hamar. Now all she knew was that he was no longer there; and she had no idea of his whereabouts.

Thinking again about her daughter-in-law, Helga said to herself : 'No, I haven't anything against her, save the fact that she has no relatives and that she has been brought up by the kindness of strangers, and, that she is rather delicate in health.' 'Probably', she thought, 'it was because of her physical delicacy that Haldor had not troubled to till the land which belonged

to him. He evidently thought that it would be better for him
to do some hunting, and to combine it with other jobs now and
again, down there in the big village. He was a hard worker,
and did his best to support his family. 'But', she thought, 'if
his illness goes on for a long time it would have been good if
his own land had been in good condition.' His illness was
caused by a bad fall in August, near St Bartholomew's Day. He
had been confined to bed from August to the 23rd of Novem-
ber. Then he made a partial recovery. But the week before he
had gone a little way into the forest to see if he could do some
hunting, and bring home some fresh meat, and a skin which
he could barter for flour and bacon. But when he came back
that evening, he was so exhausted that he had to be helped
into bed. Since then he had been worse than ever. Helga went
over to see how he was. He was awake, his cheeks were
flushed with fever, and his eyes showed how ill he had been.
'Mother,' he said, as she bent over him, 'my traps are outside,
on this night of all nights!' His mother answered him rather
shortly, 'I know, but it's not your fault'; she added more
gently: 'Now, do try to sleep my son; God knows you've done
your best!'

Ever since Christianity had come to Norway it had been the
custom that during the few days of the Christmas Festival
there should be peace between men and all living creatures. St
Olav had established this custom, and he had been very stern
with people who left their traps and snares out in the open
during those few days.

A little later his mother said: 'Perhaps we can arrange it
after all, Haldor? We might find someone to go up into the
mountain to disconnect them? Or perhaps, I could do it myself? You've put them in Rundvatstal, haven't you?' Haldor
lay with his eyes shut and he murmured faintly, 'Is it too late
to go tonight?' 'It's already quite dark,' said his mother. Haldor
half whispered: 'They'll be easy to find, I didn't go far away—
there are seven ptarmigan snares, above the brook, and one for
the lynxes, just under the group of larches, and one on the
other side of the moor in the opposite direction.'

His mother did not reply. A little later Haldor seemed to have fallen asleep again. Then Helga whispered to the little girls: 'You may eat whatever is left over on your father's plate,' for she knew they were casting longing glances at the morsels of bread floating on the fish soup. Helga knew that she had plenty of bread for the main feast days, and enough meat for the next day.

A little later, her son woke up and began to moan: 'Oh, Mother, my back feels as if it's being cut in two with a knife! I don't believe the pain will leave me until my traps have been removed, and I feel almost suffocated.' His mother said quietly: 'You know, Haldor, on this Holy Night no Christian ought to be out-of-doors either on the mountain-side or in the valley.' 'Yes, yes!' he murmured, but she saw the sweat was pouring from him. She had already sent the little girls to bed, and they were on the brink of falling asleep when, suddenly, their father cried out so loudly that they were startled, and rather frightened. 'Haldor, you must try to control yourself,' said his mother. 'Yes I know,' he said, 'but I can't help it.' After a few minutes, the children settled down again and fell asleep. 'Haldor,' said his mother very quietly, 'you know how it is? I would willingly go out and do this for you, but just think what it would mean for Signe and the children—if you don't get better—and I am not there.' Her son gave her a look of understanding, but he said nothing.

His mother felt almost desperate when she saw him biting his lips and clenching his fists with pain, with the sweat pouring from him. She tried to argue with herself: What ought she to do? She knew that this Holy Night was the most dangerous in the whole year. Even in the larger villages no one went out of doors at this time, excepting to go to church. Everyone put the sign of the cross on his door for protection, for everyone believed that the powers of evil were abroad on this night, and that it would go ill with anyone who had not been shriven. Suddenly she started up, she must have been almost dozing off to sleep. Haldor was awake: 'Is the pain very bad?' she asked. He nodded his head. And as she sat there by his bedside some lines of a hymn which she had learnt and sung as a child came back to her. It was something about 'the medicine for all our sins'. And then she remembered that she must have learnt it from a boy who later went into a monastery in the south of Norway.

Haldor had dropped off to sleep again, but he moaned in his sleep, and tossed and turned. And then she began to think about this hymn. Why had it come into her mind at that moment? 'Is it', she wondered, 'to remind me that there is One who is stronger than all ghosts and evil spirits?' Then she thought, 'Surely it would be a good deed to go out into the night and remove the traps, that nothing may disturb the peace of Christmas.'

Suddenly she got up, stood still for a moment, deep in thought. Then she made the sign of the cross over her son, and over the two little girls, fast asleep in their bed in the corner. She banked up the fire, and blew out the Christmas Candle. 'I am going out into this night in God's Name.'

Outside a faint light gleamed over the white world. The moon had risen and was shining behind the clouds. Helga found Haldor's skis and bound them on her feet. The top crust of snow crackled beneath her feet, for it had just frozen over again. Above her on the meadow there was a wall of snow, higher than the fence round the house. Helga went in that direction and soon she was out on the white expanse of the moor. And as she flew along on the skis she repeated short prayers, and some lines from a Latin hymn, in time with her movements. She wasn't quite sure what this hymn meant, but she thought it was strange that these lines should have come into her mind after forty years, on such a night as this.

At first she was not at all anxious; she found the motion easy and pleasant. Very soon she found the seven ptarmigan snares; they were in a copse of birches near the brook. But when she went further, the going was difficult. From time to time there was enough light to see the peaks of the mountains above her, and that enabled her to keep on in the right direction. Then she came into dark patches, and when she stood

still it seemed as though the air was full of rushing sounds.
She began to feel afraid: 'Suppose a lynx should come out and
attack me?' But she did not give way to panic. She made the
sign of the cross and went on again. When the way lay through
the fir trees, she lost her sense of direction, and a little later
she came into a thick white mist. She knew that this was
dangerous, and if it did not lift she would not be able to get
home that night, or perhaps even next day. For this was thick
fog, which had come up from the valley. Suddenly her skis
caught on some object which gave out a metallic sound. She
bent down and found it was one of Haldor's traps. She heaved
a sigh of relief, and thanked heaven that she now knew where
she was. She realized that she must climb as high as possible
in order to get away from the mist: then, God helping her, she
would be in no danger of getting lost once more. She found
that the traps were in disorder, so she picked them up—
though they were heavy to carry—and began to climb further
up the hill. At last she reached the ridge for which she was
making. There was very little snow there and the fog lay
beneath her like a weird white sea. Suddenly, on the opposite
ridge, she saw a bright light, and realized it came from a great
blazing fire. Strange sounds drifted over to her and she was
terribly afraid. She buried her face in her hands, and prayed
and prayed: 'Deliver us from evil, oh God! Thou art my strong
defence. Have mercy upon me!' Then she heard a sound of
singing. At first she dared not listen, but after a while she took
her hands away from her ears and listened quietly. Yes, these
were *good* sounds! This was Christmas music. She knew this
from the tunes which she had often heard in church. Could
this be the work of evil spirits? No, that was the voice of a
strong man, she thought, and as she listened the singing ceased,
the door on the opposite ridge was closed, and again all was
still on the mountain-side. Helga sat down, huddled up in her
cloak and wraps. For a long time she sat quite still and the
melody of the carols echoed and re-echoed in her mind. Then
she dozed off for a time. When she woke up she saw a great
star over-head. She stood up, stretched her stiff legs and arms

and then knelt down and worshipped God, free from all fear, for now she knew that God was stronger than all the evil forces in the world. After this, for a long time, she sat and watched the sky and the stars. At last she said her night prayers and lay down to catch a little sleep before setting out on her return journey. For now she felt very tired.

She slept and dreamed wonderful dreams in which her own people were mixed up with the Virgin Mary and many of the saints, and Zachariah, and the rest of the holy men and women in the Bible.

*   *   *

Helga opened her eyes and closed them again because the light was too bright: the sky above her was a dazzling blue and the snow shone so brilliantly that her eyes could not stand it; it seemed to glow and glitter with pale gold and crystal, while the transparent blue shadows, and the green of the forest trees was so intense that it too seemed to shine and glow. Yet, when she opened her eyes once more—because a shadow seemed to have come between her and the dazzling brightness—she saw a man's face bending over her, a round face, tanned and healthy, with fair curly hair and a curly red beard. It was Olav, her eldest son, and she was lying in his arms. She closed her eyes again, she felt she dared not look up. She didn't know whether she was on this earth or not. Whatever *had* happened to a poor, sinful, unimportant woman like her?

And now Olav shook her gently, and went on rubbing her hands and arms: 'Mother, Mother, are you better now? Mother, whatever are you doing up here on the moor? However did you get here?' Helga sat up and rubbed her eyes, all around was a brilliant winter day and Olav was kneeling in the snow beside her, and there were her skis and a snare, and his leather jacket, upon which she was lying, and there lay one of the traps for the lynx. While Olav was rubbing her, he went on, half-laughing and half-crying, 'My God, Mother, however did you get here?' Her limbs were so stiff and cold that when he helped her to her feet he had to support her under her shoulders as the two of them began to descend through the forest.

Then Olav told her that a friend in the large village had sent a message through someone else that Olav Arnesson, if he could be found, was urgently needed at home, as his brother was ill and his mother was getting very tired with all the extra work and anxiety, which was too much for her at her age. This message had reached him at the farm at Nidaros. He had started out at once, hoping to reach the church in his home village by Christmas Eve. But when he got caught in the fog, he had to shelter in the old hut on the ridge. 'Yes,' he said, answering her questions, 'it was my fire you saw. I shouted, but as there was no answer I began to sing my Christmas carol, partly to reassure myself.' He felt it was rather creepy to be alone in the winter darkness up there on the hillside. Then he went inside the hut and fell asleep, and when he woke up in the morning and went outside and looked round he saw some skis sticking up in the snow. So he hurried over, thinking someone might have met with an accident. And so he had found her!

At last they came out of the forest and saw the farmhouse beneath them, in the brightness of the morning sunshine. There was Signe, standing on the little strip between the house and the outbuildings, and with her were the two little girls. The young wife shaded her eyes with her hand and looked up to see who was coming. As they drew nearer they could see that she had been crying a great deal.

The moment they had greeted each other with smiles and tears of relief the grandmother said: 'But how is Haldor?' His wife said, he was fast asleep when she got back. After High Mass she had been given a lift, so she got back sooner than she expected, and the little girls were as good as gold, waiting for her, and they all sat down and drank milk and ate their rolls as happy as could be! Soon after that Haldor woke and said that he felt better. But both of them were very anxious about his mother who still had not returned, said

Signe, as she looked in wonder at this strange man, her brother in law, and the children hid behind her and peeped out at him. But the grandmother spoke firmly to them, and said they had to come out and say how-do-you-do nicely to their uncle. Then Olav picked up the youngest in his arms and carried her into the house to see his brother.

Haldor turned to his mother and said: 'I guessed that you had succeeded in carrying out your purpose and had found the traps and snares, for all of a sudden my pain stopped, and a refreshing sense of repose came over me.'

Olav sat by his brother with a little girl on each knee. The children were speechless and went on gazing at their uncle who had given each of them a silver ring. Haldor lay there and looked at the luggage his brother had brought with him. But Olav had also brought a great deal of money with him, which he gave at once to his mother.

Signe went about her household duties and rocked the baby's cradle now and again while she saw to it that the soup was being heated over the fire. Helga was so overcome with fatigue and joy that she cried quietly for a time; then she went into a corner of the room, knelt down, and tried to find words to thank God for the happiest Christmas that a poor sinful old woman had ever experienced here upon earth.

9 · An Exile's Story

NIKOLAI LESSKOV

Many years ago, in Czarist Russia, a man was travelling through Siberia. One day while he was staying with a Russian family in a remote village his host, a very quiet person, told him the following story:

OUR district is one of the places in Siberia to which exiles are sent as a punishment for political offences, or for other reasons. But in spite of this it is not a bad place to live in, with a life of its own and plenty of trade. My father settled here as a young man in the days when serfdom was still the rule in Russia—so you can see how long ago that was! I myself was born here. We have always been fairly well off, and even now we are not poor. We belong to the Mother Church of Russia and we hold firmly to the simple faith of our fathers. My father was a great reader, and he taught me to love books and knowledge. So it came about that all my friends were people who had the same taste. In my youth I had a very true friend, Timothy Ossipovitch, and it is his story I want to tell you.

When he came to us, Timothy was still a young man. I was eighteen at the time, and he was a little older. He was a young man of excellent character, and you may wonder why he had been banished to Siberia. In a village like ours we never asked an exile why he was there. It might be too embarrassing. But so far as we could understand this is what had happened: Timothy was an orphan, and had been brought up by his uncle, who was his legal guardian. When Timothy was about seventeen he found that nearly all his fortune had been either wasted or simply used selfishly by his uncle. When he discovered this, he was so angry that in a quarrel he fired at his uncle. Fortunately he only wounded him in the hand. The judge treated Timothy leniently on account of his youth, so he was exiled to Siberia, and indeed to my own village.

Now although Timothy had lost nine-tenths of his inheritance, the tenth was enough to keep him in some comfort. He built a small house close to us, and settled down. But the injustice he had suffered still affected him very deeply. He was so angry and resentful that he could not lead a normal life. For a long time he lived like a recluse; he refused to make any contact with his neighbours. He shut himself up in his house; the only people he saw were the couple who looked after him. He spent his time reading book after book, most of them on serious subjects, and especially on religion. At last there came a day when I was able to talk with him over the fence—then later, he asked me to come to his house—from that time I often went to see him, and we became very good friends.

At first my parents were not very pleased with me for making friends with Timothy. 'We don't know who he is or why he hides himself from everybody. We do hope he won't do you any harm.' But when I told my parents the kind of man he was, how we read religious books together, and talked about the Faith, they were satisfied that there could not be anything seriously wrong with him. Then my father visited him, and invited Timothy to come to see us. At once my parents saw that he was a good fellow and they began to like him. Indeed, they were very sorry for him, because he was always brooding over the wrong that had been done to him; if anyone happened to mention the uncle, Timothy would go as white as a sheet, and look as though he were about to faint. He was a very honourable man, and had a good mind; but owing to this bitterness of spirit he could not settle to any useful work.

However, when he fell in love with my sister this extreme

bitterness passed away. He married her, gave up his melan-
choly brooding, and began to live and prosper; he went into
business and became wealthy. After ten years everyone in the
district knew and respected him. He built a new house with
large rooms. He had everything he needed, his wife was very
capable, and he had healthy, delightful children. What more
could he want? It seemed as though all the troubles of his
youth were over and forgotten. But one day when we were
out driving in his pony-cart I suddenly asked him: 'Brother
Timothy, are you now quite happy in your mind?' 'What do
you mean?' he said, looking at me with a strange look on his
face.

'Have you recovered everything you lost in your youth?'

He went very white, and said nothing; but he went on
driving through the forest. After some moments of silence I
said: 'Forgive me, brother, for asking this question. I thought
all that trouble was over long ago . . . over and forgotten?'
'That's not the point,' he answered, 'it makes no difference that
it happened so long ago. It is over, yes, but I still keep thinking
about it.'

I felt very sorry for him, for I now saw that although
Timothy knew the Scriptures so well, and could talk elo-
quently about religion, he still nursed the memory of this
injustice in his heart. 'Surely', I thought, 'this means that the
Word of God is of no avail to him?'

For some minutes we drove on in silence; I was deep in
thought. At last he looked at me and said: 'What are you
thinking about?' 'Oh, all sorts of things!' I said, rather lightly.

'I don't believe it! I believe you are thinking about me?'

'Well, yes, I *am* thinking about you.'

'Tell me what you are thinking about me!'

'Please don't be cross with me, brother, this is what I have
been thinking: You know the Scriptures, yet your heart is
full of resentment and anger, and you will not submit to God.
Does this mean that all your reading of the Bible has done you
no good?'

Timothy wasn't angry with me, but his face darkened and

he said: 'You don't know the Bible well enough to say this kind of thing.' Then he began to argue with me, trying to justify himself. He said I was too ignorant of the Bible and of the world, to understand him. I agreed. He went on to say: 'There are injustices which no honourable man can put up with.' Then he added: 'I have never spoken about this to any one, but because you are my friend I will tell you. My uncle caused so much pain and sorrow to my father and mother that in the end my mother died of it. My uncle slandered my father; above all he spread such lies about me that he prevented me from marrying a young girl I had loved from childhood, and all this because he, an older man, wanted to marry her himself. Can anyone forget such an injury?' he asked. 'I will *never* forgive him, *never*!'

'You certainly have had a raw deal,' I replied. 'I agree, but this does not alter the fact that you aren't getting any help from all your study of the Holy Scriptures.' Then he launched into a long argument about my scanty knowledge of the Bible and of all the passages in the Old Testament where good men stood up for themselves and even killed their enemies! The poor fellow was trying to justify himself in my eyes.

'Timothy,' I said, 'I know I am only a simple fellow, and not like you. Yet even I can see that there is a great difference between the Old and the New Testament; there's a lot about revenge in the Old Testament, but in the New Testament it's all about love and forgiveness.' He was silent. Then I went on, very quietly, to remind him of the way our Lord was treated in his Passion: how he was beaten and ill-treated and insulted and put to death by his enemies. But he forgave them all. Timothy was not offended by my frank speech. After further conversation he pressed my hand and said: 'I can't help it! Stop talking about forgiveness, you are only making me very sad.' I stopped at once, for I could see that he was very unhappy. But I was sure that one day he would change. Now this came about in a most remarkable way.

At that time Timothy had been in Siberia for sixteen years; he was about thirty-seven. He had a good wife, three children, and a pleasant life. He was very fond of flowers, especially roses—there were roses everywhere, in the garden, and in the house. Indeed, the whole house was full of their beauty and their fragrance. In summer he always went into the garden about sunrise. First he examined his roses, to see if they needed any attention, then he sat down among them on a bench, took out a book, and began to read. I believe he often said his prayers there as he sat in the early morning sunshine. One day he was sitting there as usual, reading his New Testament, and he came to the passage where Christ went to a rich man's house, and his host did not even give him water to wash his feet. Timothy put the book down and began to think, and as he brooded over the great poverty and love of the Lord he burst out, 'Oh Lord! if you were to come to me I would give you all I have and am!' Suddenly a wind passed over the roses and he seemed to hear the words: 'I will come.'

Later in the morning Timothy came over to see me and told me what had happened. He said anxiously: 'Do you believe that the Lord will really come to me as a guest?' I replied, 'That, brother, is quite beyond my understanding! Is there anything about it in the Holy Scripture?' Timothy said, 'Well, he is the same Christ, today and for ever. I don't dare to refuse to believe it.'

'Well, then,' I said, 'believe it!'

Timothy reflected for a few moments, then he turned to me and said: 'I know what I'll do. I'll have a place set for him at our table every day.' This did not seem to me quite the right line to take, but I felt I could not suggest anything else, so I shrugged my shoulders and said, 'You must do what you think right.'

Timothy told his wife that from the next day he wished an extra place to be prepared at every family meal; this sixth place was to be put at the head of the table for an honoured guest, and a special armchair as well. She was astonished, and very curious: 'Whom do you expect?' she asked. But Timothy kept his own counsel; he merely told her and the rest of the household that he had ordered this because he had made a vow, 'for the most honoured guest who may arrive'. No one knew what he meant, and they were left wondering.

Day after day Timothy waited for the Lord: next day, then the following Sunday, but nothing happened. Sometimes he waited in a fever of impatience, but he never doubted that the Lord would come, as he had said. One day he came to me and said: 'Brother, day after day I pray: "Lord come", and I wait, but so far I have never heard the answer for which I long: "Yes, I will come soon".'

Secretly I felt uncertain how to answer Timothy when he talked like this. Sometimes I was afraid that my friend had become 'puffed up', and that this was a temptation which had come to him. But Providence meant it otherwise.

Six months passed, and Christmas was approaching. It was a hard winter. On Christmas Eve Timothy came to me and said: 'My dear brother, tomorrow I am expecting the Lord!' I said simply: 'And why are you so sure of it this time?' 'This time', he said, 'after I had prayed the usual prayer, my whole soul was moved, and I seemed to hear very clearly the words "Yes, I am coming soon". Tomorrow is his festival. Could there be a better day for him to come? I want you to be there, with all our relatives, for I feel awed and afraid.'

'Timothy,' I said, 'you know that I don't profess to understand this matter, and I certainly don't expect you to see the Lord, sinful man as I am—but you are part of our family and I will come. But may I say something else? Since you expect such a Royal Guest would it not be wise to invite not only your own relatives and friends, but the sort of company that he would desire?'

Timothy smiled and said: 'I see what you mean. Yes, I'll send out my servants into the whole village to invite all the exiles who are in need and poverty here, so far from their homeland. It is only fitting that when the Lord comes he should find the kind of guests he would want to see.'

So on Christmas Day we all went to Timothy's house a little later than was usual, for a midday meal. We found all the large rooms filled with people, typical Siberians, that is, people

who were exiles from their own countries. There were men
and women, and many of the younger generation as well,
people of very varied callings and from different regions,
Russians, and Poles, and even some from far-away Esthonia.
Timothy had arranged that all the exiles who had not yet
found their feet in a strange land should be invited. The long
tables were covered with fresh white linen cloths, and all sorts
of good things were placed there for the guests. The maids
bustled about and brought in meat-pasties and kvass for the
first course. Outside, the short winter day was drawing to
a close, and all the guests were assembled. No one else
was expected. A snow-storm had begun, and the wind
swept round the house; it was a terrible storm. Only the one
Guest was missing: the One for whom they were waiting.
The candles were lit, and the guests were about to take their
places at the table. Outside, it was not quite dark and inside
the house, apart from the candles the rest of the rooms were
in semi-darkness; the only light came from the little lamps
burning before the ikons. Timothy kept moving about from
one room to another; he could not sit still, he was so agitated:
'Could it be', he wondered, 'that after all the Guest would not
come?'

He whispered to me, 'I can't make it out. Perhaps I have
misunderstood the message? Well, we must go forward in
God's Name. We must give thanks and start the meal.'

Timothy stood up and went to the ikon and began to pray
the Lord's Prayer aloud. Then he added, 'Christ is born today!
Let us praise the Lord our God! Christ has come down from
heaven, let us all rejoice that the Most High has visited us, and
is even now in our midst.'

He had hardly finished these words when there came a great
gust of wind which shook the house, followed by a loud noise,
as if something had fallen against the door; suddenly, the door
burst open of itself. The guests were so frightened that they
left the tables and huddled together in a corner; some fell
down on the floor, others stood still and looked at the doorway. On the threshold stood a very old man dressed in rags; he

was so weak that he could hardly stand. He was leaning on the nearest chair in the room; but behind him there was a wonderful light, and a delicate fragrance seemed to come in with him. Some people thought they saw a little lamp, burning with a steady flame unmoved by the wind.

As Timothy gazed at this strange figure, he cried out: 'Lord! I see him, and I receive him in thy Name! Do not come to me thyself, for I am not worthy that thou shouldest come under my roof.' He knelt down, and bowed his face to the ground. Then he cried out in a loud voice: 'Let us rejoice, for Christ himself is among us!' And all the guests said, *Amen*.

Fresh candles were brought into the room, and Timothy stood up and looked intently at the old man. The radiance and the fragrance had faded; only the old man remained. Timothy went forward, took him by both hands and led him to the empty place reserved for the guest of honour. He knew who he was: his old uncle, who had done him so much harm. As they sat down together the other guests went back to the Feast. Then the old man told Timothy that his whole life had gone to pieces; he had lost his family and all his possessions. For a long time he had been wandering about the forests and plains of Siberia, trying to find his nephew, for he wanted to ask Timothy to forgive him. He longed for this, though he was frightened of Timothy's anger. In the snow-storm he had lost

F

his way completely, and he was so cold he was afraid he would freeze to death that night. 'Suddenly', he said, 'I met someone who said to me: "Go to that house, over there, where you see the lights. Take my place, and you will be warmed and fed; you may eat out of my plate!" Then he took hold of both my hands, and helped me. Somehow, I don't know how, I reached this door.'

'Uncle,' said Timothy, 'I know *who* led you here. It was the Lord who said that . . . so you are welcome to the best place at the Feast. Eat and drink in his Name, and I invite you to stay as long as you like, to the very end of your life.'

So the old man remained with Timothy and when he was dying he blessed his nephew. And Timothy had peace in his heart for he had learned to obey the words of the Lord: 'Love your enemies, do good to those who ill-treat you . . .' 'Come Lord Jesus! Come quickly and abide with me.'

10 · The Sacrifice

HENRI BORDEAUX

D R Brunoy, who had conducted his medical colleagues to the door, stood on the threshold saying in his tired voice, 'Then you can't suggest any other treatment?'

The two physicians looked at one another; then the elder man answered: 'Unfortunately, the last two injections have been unsuccessful, we have done everything we could, we can't do any more!'

'Nothing more? . . . do you think the child will live much longer?' 'Longer?' said the other man looking extremely surprised; shrugging his shoulders he added laconically, 'a few hours'. The older doctor said, 'Some hours . . . one never knows', for experience had made him cautious, 'but anyhow the child will not suffer'.

The two colleagues put on their fur coats, got into their sledge, and wrapped themselves up warmly in their rugs. Dr Brunoy thanked them courteously for coming so far to help him. The younger man took out his watch to see the time, for he wanted to get back to the town as soon as possible; for it was Christmas, the loveliest family festival in the year, and he longed for the peace of his own home.

The horses were champing impatiently and the moment that the coachman touched the whip they were off like a streak of lightning. Dr Brunoy stood perfectly still upon the step, looking after them; his last hope disappeared when the sledge was out of sight. Then he turned round and went into the house. But before he went upstairs to his wife, who was sitting by the bedside of the dying child, he searched through his medical books once more to see if he could find anything more to be tried. Was there *really* no hope?

Outside the light was fading. Dr Brunoy looked out of his window at the little town lying below, and then up to the mountains and the forest, white with snow. In a flash he saw the years that had passed since he came to this remote place. He came there first of all because the place was so remote that he need not fear competition. But the people of the whole district had welcomed him as their deliverer. Their welcome was so heartfelt that within a year this little place was 'home', both to him and his wife. Their happiness was increased by the birth of their sturdy little son. Very soon patients came to him from far and wide. There was a good deal of ignorance among the peasant women, and too many children died because the doctor was not called in time. Dr Brunoy tried his hardest to instruct the mothers in child-care, and to some extent his work had already borne fruit in a reduced rate of infant- and child-mortality.

And now his own child was dying of diphtheria. He had saved the lives of many children, but now he could not save his own son. When his wife heard his step on the stairs she called out, 'Oh, do come, he's worse!' There she sat with the Christmas crib on the table beside the bed, and the child's presents lying on the floor, but the little boy was far beyond noticing anything. His wife looked up at her husband with a question in her eyes. He looked at her gravely, and then said very quietly, 'He's dying.' 'What can we do?' 'Nothing, except wait for the end.' There was silence in the room. As the room grew darker the mother got up and went out of the room and came back with a shaded lamp in her hand.

At six o'clock the young maid opened the door very quietly and said, 'A man from Roselande has come, he wants to see the doctor.' 'I can't see anyone, Mariette,' said the doctor. A little later the girl came back and whispered: 'He says he won't go, he *must* speak to you himself.' Dr Brunoy immediately left the room in order to send this importunate visitor away. He found him in the kitchen, warming himself by the stove. Melting snow was streaming from his shoulders over his rough cloak. The peasant turned his thin serious face towards the doctor.

'Oh, it's *you*,' said the doctor. 'What do you want?' The man replied: 'My child is ill.' 'I'll come early tomorrow morning,' said the doctor. But Rivaz shook his head. 'Without you he will not live through the night.' 'I'll come very early,' said the doctor, 'but my own child is dying, I can't come this evening.' 'But my child is dying too,' said Rivaz. And both men fell silent, each deep in his own misery. Then, very quietly, Rivaz said: 'You want to heal your boy but not mine.' 'No,' said the doctor, sadly, 'my child is doomed.' Another pregnant silence followed. Once more Rivaz spoke: '*My* boy is not doomed. He is the child of my old age, and I shall have no more children!'

'I will come early tomorrow morning, I *promise* you,' the doctor repeated, but the older man only said sorrowfully: 'Then it will be too late.' Again the two men stood there in silence, till the doctor flared up and said, 'I *can't* leave my child until he dies, don't you *understand*, Rivaz?'

The peasant took up his old felt hat in his trembling fingers, hesitated for a moment, and then moved towards the door. As he went he murmured under his breath, 'So two children will die,' but he spoke very quietly, with a kind of deep resignation, as if this were irrevocable. 'Wait a moment!' the doctor called out. The man turned back and faced him. 'Is he coughing a great deal?' he asked. 'He did,' said the peasant, 'but is now much less, is that a good sign, doctor?' 'No,' said the doctor. 'But you must see', he pleaded, 'that I simply can't come? How is his breathing?' 'It sounds like a whistle and sometimes it seems as though he will suffocate.' 'Just as it was last night with Jean. Does he have these suffocating attacks very often?' 'Yes.' 'I'm terribly sorry for you.' 'Is it too late?' 'No, he might recover.'

Suddenly in a sentence the peasant said what was in his heart. 'You can't do anything more for *your* child, but you can still do something for mine.' After a moment's silence the doctor looked the other father straight in the face; his look became resolute, and in a firm voice he said: 'I'll come with you, Rivaz.'

He turned and went quickly upstairs to see his little Jean. The child was scarcely breathing, and was very pale. Then he turned to his wife, and handed her a little bottle: 'Charlotte, take this and hold it to his mouth, it will ease his breathing, we can't do any more.'

'Why do you talk like this?'

'Because I must go out.'

'What now, tonight?'

'The little boy at Roselande is seriously ill, I may be able to save his life.'

'And our Jean?'

'His life is no longer in our hands, you can look after him as well as I can.'

'Don't go,' she pleaded. She was so distressed that she cried out, 'You don't love your wife, and you don't love our child.' 'Oh my darling,' he said with deep compassion, greatly moved, but his wife was nearly beside herself and she wouldn't listen to him. He bent over the child, stroked his cheek very gently. Then very rapidly, as though he were afraid that his courage would not hold out, he strode out of the room.

During the drive the two men did not speak a word. From time to time Rivaz had to pull hard at the reins and urge the horse on with encouraging cries, for the poor animal was very tired.

The road was little more than a cart-track; much of it led through a deep gully, surrounded by great pine trees. In the distance they could hear the sound of falling water. Two lamps had been fastened to the front of the sledge and the lights swayed to and fro and lit up the trees and rocks in the forest. After an hour's journey they drew up before an isolated house. The family had heard the sound of the sledge, and the door was at once opened; a woman with a lantern in her hand was looking out for them: 'Is the doctor there?' she called out. 'Yes,' said her husband. She breathed a sigh of relief and ushered the two men into the sick room. Some time later the doctor packed up his instruments and began to get ready to leave.

'Do you think he'll recover?' asked the mother.

'I think so: I'll come again in the morning.'

'Must you go back immediately?' asked Rivaz.

'Yes, at once.'

The father was deeply moved, and he produced a golden coin, which he had saved up for years, and held it out to the doctor. But Dr Brunoy shook his head and smiled gravely: 'No, my good friend, he said, 'no one can *pay* me for the journey I have made tonight.'

On the return drive the two men were quite silent. On the way back through the forest they met several groups of people carrying lanterns, and the lights twinkled through the trees. The people from the surrounding villages and hamlets were on their way to Midnight Mass. Now and again they were singing an old carol:

> *The Holy Child is born today,*
> *O Christian men rejoice!*

And when they met the sledge they called out, 'A blessed Christmas!'

The doctor did not feel able to answer them, and Rivaz said nothing, although in his heart he was very thankful.

At one of the cross-roads in the forest, not far from the little town, the light from the lanterns lit up a large cross by the wayside. A few snowflakes were falling gently. The form of the Crucified Lord stood out very plainly in this light, and it seemed to the doctor that a healing light shone from the thorn-crowned head. Then Dr Brunoy remembered the words of the ancient hymn 'Unto us a Child is born' . . . suddenly he was filled with peace: all his questioning was over—all rebellion had ceased. He knew that he had done his duty, he had been able to save the Rivaz child. He was quite sure he would not see his own child alive, but this caused him no bitterness; his heart was at rest.

When he reached his home and went into the sick room he found his wife bending over the bed. He went up to her and said very gently and kindly, 'My beloved Charlotte!' 'You weren't there!' she sobbed, and then she looked into his eyes, and as she did so she too felt a great peace flowing from him into her sad heart. She leant on him, and in the quietness she too felt sure that with him she would find the courage she needed to go on living, and even to love life once more.

11 · *The Three Dark Kings*

WOLFGANG BORCHERT

LATE one night a man was wandering through the dark streets on the fringe of a large town. There was no moon, but he could see the outline of the houses against the night sky. As he walked along the pavement his steps echoed with a hollow sound. As he crossed the road at a certain point he stumbled over something on the ground. He bent down and fingered it; it was an old plank of wood, thrown away to rot. He kicked it hard and a large piece broke off. He picked it up to take home. The wood had a curious, sweetish smell. Then he walked on again; now and then in the narrow streets the shadows were so dark that he had to grope his way. In these patches of darkness it seemed to him that there was no light anywhere: no lighted windows, no moon, no stars.

When he reached his home, as he opened the door the blue eyes of his young wife met his, with a questioning look on her tired face. Her breath steamed out into the room, for it was bitterly cold. Her husband knelt down before the stove and broke the wood into small pieces, which sent out a fragrance into the room: 'Smells good!' he said. 'Almost like cake!' And he began to laugh. His wife gave him a warning look. 'Don't laugh,' she said, 'he's asleep.'

The man turned once more to the stove and put some more wood upon the fire and soon a soft radiance seemed to fill the little room. For a moment the firelight lit up the tiny face of the new-born child. The father looked at it with wonder. 'His little round face looks all right to me,' he thought. 'It's got everything it ought to have: a nose and a mouth and two eyes.

I believe his eyes are large,' he said to himself. He went on looking at him, fascinated. The baby's mouth was open, and he was breathing gently through his lips, but his nose and ears were red with cold. His wife looked across the room to her husband; she seemed to answer his thoughts, as she murmured quietly, 'At any rate he is alive,' and the baby slept on.

The man got up and went to the cupboard: 'I see we've still got some oatmeal left,' he said, turning to his wife. 'Yes,' she said, 'that's one good thing.' Her husband bent down and put some more wood upon the fire. 'Now that she has her child', he thought, 'can they both survive the cold?' A wave of intense anger swept over him. 'Why should we be in such distress? Who is to blame?' He wanted to throw the blame on someone. But he felt confused and bewildered and did not know what to think. The next time that he put some more wood on the fire a gleam of light fell on the face of the sleeping child: 'Look!' said his mother, 'isn't that like a halo?' 'Some halo!' he thought bitterly; and again he wondered who was to blame for their misery? Involuntarily he clenched his fists, and his heart was heavy.

A few moments later there was a knock on the door. Startled by the sound in the dead of night he opened the door and saw dimly the shapes of three men on the doorstep. One of them said quietly, 'We saw the light through the window. May we come in and rest for a little while?' 'We've got a new baby,' said the man, 'but do come in.' The strangers did not reply, but they stepped quietly into the room. 'We'll be very quiet', they whispered as they sat down on a wooden bench near the stove. As they sat there the firelight fell on their faces.

There were three of them, in three old uniforms. One man was carrying a cardboard box, one had a sack thrown over his shoulder; the third man had no hands: 'Frozen', he said lifting up the stumps for them to see. Then he turned to the young father and said: 'There's some tobacco in my coat-pockets and some thin paper. Will you kindly take it out and give it to my comrades?' His two friends took the tobacco and paper and began rolling cigarettes. But the young mother looked anxious, and she said gently: 'Please don't smoke in here! It would be very bad for the baby.' The strangers nodded and the four men went outside and stood there smoking. One of the strangers had both feet heavily bandaged; he opened his sack and took out a piece of wood: 'Look! This is a donkey. It took me several months to carve. It's for the baby,' and he handed it to the father. 'What's the matter with your feet?' said the father. 'Dropsy,' he said laconically, 'from starvation.'

'And what's the matter with the other one?' looking at the third man: 'Nothing,' he whispered, in a trembling voice, 'it's only my nerves. I've gone through too much strain and anxiety.' The four men stood silent for a moment; then they dropped their cigarette ends on the stone step, stamped out the sparks, and went back into the house.

The three men came in very quietly, crossed the room, and looked down on the face of the sleeping child. The man whose 'nerves were bad' opened the cardboard box with his shaky hands and took out a yellow sweet. 'That's for the mother and the little one.' The young mother was frightened when she saw the three dark figures bending over the baby. But the baby pushed so hard against her breast and cried so lustily that the three men at once turned to go. They walked softly across the room. At the door they turned, nodded, and went out into the night.

The father stood at the door and watched them as they stumbled down the street and disappeared into the darkness. Then he came in and shut and barred the door. There was a strange expression on his face as he turned to look at his wife: 'Strange saints,' he said. Then he moved to the fire and put on some more wood, took down the porridge saucepan from its hook, still deep in thought. 'Queer saints,' he murmured to himself. But his voice was gentle and his hands were no longer clenched in despair.

'But the baby cried so loudly,' said his wife. 'Isn't he lively?' she added proudly. The baby opened his mouth and yelled. 'Is he crying?' said the father. 'No,' she said, 'I think he's laughing!' 'The wood smells good,' said her husband as once more the curious fragrance filled the air. 'Almost like cake, very sweet.' 'And now it's Christmas Day,' said his wife. 'Ah yes! Christmas,' he murmured; and from the fire a gleam of light fell on the face of the sleeping child.

12 · *The Christ-Child of Ostrowice*

FRIEDRICH HOFFMANN

I'M a German, you know, telling you this story. (Have another drink!) And it was a German who shot this child, before our very eyes! And the man who tried to save the child and lost his own life into the bargain—he, too, was a German. Believe it or not, I swear this is the truth. And the child was a Jewish child.

It happened in Poland. We were a commando. It was our job to 'clean up' the Jews . . . another lot did the 'elimination'. In that district certain villages had been chosen as 'collection centres' for the hunted Jews. (Go on, have another drink!) This job wasn't quite so unpleasant as hunting out the gipsies. Jews don't shriek and carry on so much. They die more quietly. They believe in something, I suppose. Our boss used to say, 'Well, that's one advantage anyway.' We had to separate the people—men, women, and children, into separate groups; then they climbed into the lorries. They didn't need to take anything with them.

Now, one of our number (a man called Karl) was 'against it'. He didn't actually say so, but we all knew he was against the whole thing. After all, when you are all working together like this you can't help knowing how people feel about things. It was a pity that he was in our commando at all, and then— he couldn't understand a joke!

I was on the spot when it happened . . . and from that day to this I don't know what to make of it. So far as I can remember it must have been Advent, for the following January I was sent off to another part of the country. At the time, of course,

I never realized it *was* Advent! We had just finished 'clearing' a village. The whole village was empty : all the Jews were piled up in the lorries standing at the cross-roads in the middle of the village. On the whole these Jews were quiet; there wasn't much lamentation. I can still see it all : the whitewashed walls of the cottages, the wide roads, more like cart-tracks than roads, they were so rough. There was a thin covering of snow on the ground.

As we waited we saw the special CID man with two police-men searching one cottage after another, to be sure no one had been left behind. Suddenly, in one of the little huts he saw something moving. It was a child who had been sleeping be-hind the stove. I don't know whether he had been forgotten, or hidden there by his parents. He must have been somewhere between one and two years old. The inspector picked him up and brought him outside. The boss was getting impatient to be off and he signed to the Inspector to take the child away behind the houses (we all knew what he meant).

Suddenly Karl rushed forward shouting, 'No, no!' and he tore the child out of the policeman's arms, shrieking out, over and over again : 'It's the Christ-Child! It's the Christ-Child!' (Quite mad, wasn't it?) Some of us began to laugh, but not all. Karl ran round the houses like a lunatic, trying to find a way out of the village, but it was all 'sealed off', and he couldn't get through. And as he ran he hugged the child to his breast, and wrapped him in his own rough cloak. All the Jews in the lorries were watching, and so were we, for we knew that sometimes peoples' nerves give way. But this chap had got it badly. At last he fell down against the wall of a house; he was trembling all over. He was holding the child tightly in his arms, and he kept on calling out : 'It's the Christ-Child. It's the Christ-Child!' They simply had to shoot him, for he wouldn't let the child go. I'll never forget the sight. There he sat against the wall, with his blue eyes staring, looking like a Madonna; yes, I declare, like a Madonna! And the child was so small. The village was called Ostrowice, somewhere in the south of Poland. . . Come on, have another drink!

13 · *Christmas in Prison*

HANNS LILJE

CHRISTMAS was near. Christmas Eve in prison is so terrible because a wave of sentimentality passes through the gloomy building. Everyone thinks of his own loved ones, for whom he is longing; everyone suffers because he doesn't know how they will be celebrating the Festival of Divine and Human Love. Recollections of childhood come surging back, almost overwhelming some, especially those who are condemned to death, and who cannot help looking back at their past lives. It is no accident that in prison suicide attempts are particularly numerous on this special day; in our case, however, the most remarkable thing was the sentimental softness which came over our guards. Most of these SS men were young fellows, who were usually unnecessarily brutal in their behaviour, but when Christmas

Eve came we hardly knew them—the spirit of this evening
made such a deep impression upon them.

At this time we had a Commandant who was human.
Although he had risen from the lower ranks to be an SS officer,
he had remained an honest man, who, although he was harsh,
was not brutal, and who often granted us certain facilities,
until, on account of his humane attitude, he was removed
from his post. Essentially he made more impression on us
than his successor, who, in many respects, was also a decent
man.

On this particular evening in the year, this Commandant
had made various kind and humane actions possible; for instance, among us there was one who was condemned to
death, and was already chained. The Commandant had his
chains removed, and his violin was given back to him. This
man was a great artist, and his playing was like magic. Presently the great vaulted Hall resounded with the beautiful
strains of his violin. As evening fell, I was walking up and
down my cell, looking at a Nativity Scene which one of my
children had made for me; illuminated by a candle, and
decorated with some fir branches, it made my cell look like
Christmas. Meanwhile I was thinking about the Christmas Eve
service which I had conducted a year before in our Johannes-
kirche in Lichterfelde. It had been a memorable Christmas: a
Christmas festival almost entirely without children, for most
families had sent their children away from the city, since it
was increasingly exposed to air raids. So the men who were
left were chiefly men detained in Berlin by their war duties;
or else they were older people, many of them solitary, who
were rather indifferent to the dangers of air raids, and did not
need to take care of themselves for the sake of the other
people. In any case, it was a remarkable congregation which
gathered in the damaged ice-cold church for the service on
Christmas Eve. As I recalled the service I remembered that I
had preached on the words from the Prophet Isaiah: 'The
people that walked in darkness have seen a great light.' At the
beginning of my sermon, I had pointed out that when we were

children we used to dawdle home after the Christmas service, because we wanted to look into everybody's windows to see them lighting up their Christmas trees, until at last we reached our own home, and stood spellbound before our own dazzling Christmas tree. This year, however, all the windows are darkened, and the whole world was 'blacked out'. Then I said: 'This year, we older people, men separated from their families, solitary people, old people, must learn to celebrate Christmas apart from all childish romanticism and all sentimentality, for this year there is no room for this sort of thing'; then, with the help of this prophetic saying, I tried to make clear the real meaning of the Christmas message for ourselves, grown-up people passing through a dark and difficult time.

I had just reached this point in my reflections, and had just begun to feel a painful longing for a congregation, to whom I might preach the Christmas Gospel on this very evening, at this hard and difficult time, when suddenly, outside my door, I heard my number called. Usually when this call resounded through the wing of our prison it didn't mean anything good. Too often it meant interrogations, or ill-treatment, removal from the prison, or still worse, but although I was prepared for anything, I really couldn't imagine that they would do something terrible to me; I rose, and followed the guard who led me downstairs from my cell in the third storey. I was taken directly to the Commandant. In accordance with his usual custom he did not speak, but went on ahead to another cell. Before he entered this cell he turned to the guard and said: 'Bring number 212 to this cell too!' When the heavy cell door was opened a man rose to meet us; at once I saw in him a striking family likeness and realized that he was Count X. His brother, one of the first to be condemned after the attempt on Hitler's life, had asked, just before his execution, that I might be allowed to give him the Sacrament, a request that was naturally refused. He had been one of the most frequent attenders at my services, and on the Sunday before his arrest he had joined in divine worship and had received Holy Communion.

Quite spontaneously, forgetting where I was, I mentioned
G

this recollection to X, but the Commandant interrupted me
harshly, saying: 'I have not brought you gentlemen together
for personal conversation!' Then he added, turning to the
Count, 'You asked that a certain clergyman, your own friend,
might be allowed to visit you this evening in a pastoral
capacity. Unfortunately I have not been able to accede to this
request, but here is Dr Lilje, who will address some words to
you.' Now I saw what was expected of me. The Count replied:
'What I really want, sir, is to make my confession, and then
receive Holy Communion.' Immediately I said that I was ready
to do what was required; and the Commandant seemed to have
no objection. So a small silver cup was brought, a little wine,
and some bread—in the meantime number 212 had also been
brought into the cell. He was the violinist who was under sentence of death. The guard was sent out of the cell, so we four
men were there together.

At the Commandant's suggestion the violinist played a
Christmas chorale exquisitely, then, in this cell, and before
this congregation, I read the Gospel for Christmas Day: 'Now
it came to pass in those days there went out a decree . . .'
The violinist played another Christmas chorale; in the meantime I had been able to arrange my thoughts a little about the
passage in Isaiah which had filled my mind when I was sum-
moned downstairs. I said to my fellow-prisoners: 'This evening we are a congregation, part of the Church of Christ, and
this great word of divine promise is as true for us today, as it
was for those of a year ago, among whom, at that time, was
your own brother—and for all who this year receive it in
faith. Our chief concern is to believe that God, through Jesus
Christ, has allowed the eternal light to "arise and shine" upon
this world which is plunged in the darkness of death, and that
he will also make this Light to shine for us. At this moment, in
our cells we have practically nothing that makes the Christmas
festival so familiar and so lovely, but there is one thing left to
us: God's great promise. Let us cling to this promise, and to
him in the midst of the darkness. Here and now, in the midst of
the uncertainty of our prison life, in the shadow of death, we

will praise him by a firm and unshaken faith in his Word, which is addressed to us.' Then, in the midst of the cell, the Count knelt down upon the hard stone floor, and while I prayed aloud the beautiful old prayer of confession from Thomas à Kempis (which he himself had chosen) and then pronounced absolution, the tears were running silently down his cheeks. It was a very quiet celebration of the Sacrament full of deep confidence in God; almost palpably the wings of the Divine Mercy hovered over us, as we knelt at the altar in a prison cell on Christmas Eve. We were prisoners, in the power of the Gestapo—in Berlin. But the peace of God enfolded us: it was *real* and present, 'like a Hand laid gently upon us'.

Since the Commandant had obviously done all this without permission, and on his own personal responsibility, he could not allow any further conversation. The violinist played a closing chorale; I parted from my fellow-prisoner with a warm handshake, saying: 'God bless you, brother X.' When we reached the corridor the Commandant shook my hand twice, with an iron grip; he was deeply moved, turning to me, he said: 'Thank you! You cannot imagine what you have done for me this evening, in my sad and difficult daily work.' I was immediately taken back to my cell, but I praised God, and indeed, I praised him from my whole heart that in this building, under the shadow of death, and in the face of so much trouble and distress, a Christian congregation had assembled to celebrate Christmas. For it is possible to have every external sign of festivity and comfort and joyful celebrations, and yet not to have a true Christmas congregation, while in the shadow of death and in much trouble of heart a real Christian congregation can gather at Christmas. It is possible for the candles and the lights to blind our eyes, so that we can no longer see the essential element in Christmas; but the people who 'walk in darkness' can perhaps see it better than all who see only the lights of earth.

Upon us shines the Eternal Light,
Filling the world with radiance bright.

Shortly after Christmas Count X was sent to a concentration camp. The violinist was killed by the Gestapo during the last days before the collapse. I have completely lost sight of the Commandant who, soon after this, was removed from his post because he had proved too humane. But the memory of my Christmas service in 1944, illuminated by the consoling and eternal Light of God, still remains with me.

14 · Gabjir's First Present

A True Story from Nepal

High up in the heart of Nepal—a land where there is no Christmas—there has stood since 1959 a small Christian hospital. From the ridge behind the hospital there is a wonderful view of range after range of majestic mountains: Annapurna, the Fishtail Mountain, and many others. Their great peaks, covered with everlasting snow, soar up into the blue sky, and in winter the lower slopes are also white and sparkling.

Yet in that beautiful land there is a great deal of suffering, especially amongst the lepers. One day, as the doctor was making her usual round, a woman patient looked up at her with a tragic expression on her face: 'What is it?' said the doctor, bending over her. The woman answered: 'Oh, doctor! Please give me some medicine to make me die.' 'But why do you want to die?' said the doctor in surprise. 'You are getting better, and we believe that in time you will be well again.' The girl hesitated for a moment, and then in a low voice she said: 'The last time I went back to my village to see my family they turned me out. They stoned me out of the village . . . and they called out after me: "Don't you ever come back! If you do, you know what will happen."' This girl could have been cured, but she could not believe it, and she knew that none of her relations would ever believe it. So she was in despair.

MANY years earlier, in the same country, a man named Gabjir lived in a remote mountain village; he lived, with a number of relations, in a large family house, which had belonged to the family for generations, for they

were high-caste people and were comfortably off. This house
and this village were everything to him: it was *home*. He had
never been anywhere else; he had never seen a foreigner. He
knew almost nothing of the world outside Nepal. The years
passed by, and Gabjir was no longer young. One day one of
his sisters looked at him suspiciously and said: 'What's wrong
with your hands? They look funny to me.' Gabjir tried to
cover them up, murmuring, 'It's nothing. They are only a little
swollen with the cold.' A few weeks later one of his brothers
said: 'Why are you limping? Have you hurt your feet?'
Gabjir gave an evasive answer. But now the whole family was
suspicious; they watched him all the time, and he began to
feel desperate. At last the signs of leprosy became too evident
to be hidden any longer. The fear of leprosy—so strong in
Nepal—overcame all other feelings. His relatives rose up in a
body and drove Gabjir out of the village, shouting after him,
'If you come back we'll kill you.'

Gabjir wandered away from the village feeling utterly lost.
He had no home and no family any more. Where was he to go?
For the moment he tried to find a shelter for the night and
soon took refuge in an empty cattle-shed not far from his
home. He spent several days there, drinking water from the
stream near by, and subsisting on fruit which he found on the
surrounding bushes. He seemed to be living in a bad dream
and he slept a great deal. Early one morning he was wakened
by a great noise outside; his brothers had discovered his hide-
out. 'Get up and get out!' they shouted, 'and mind you never
come back! If you do we'll kill you.'

Gabjir got up at once and began to walk away along the
narrow mountain track. When he looked back one or two
stones were flung after him; he hurried on, and as he was about
to turn a corner he looked back once more: there stood his
brothers, waiting to see him disappear.

For many weeks he wandered unhappily about among the
mountains. He had never been so far from home before, and
he did not know where to go. It all seemed the same to him, for
he was now not only ill, but an outcast. He dared not go

through any village and if he met anyone on the way he shrank back and did not speak. His spirits dropped lower and lower. He could see no way out and no way forward. One day, as he was crossing a little wooden bridge over a river, he suddenly thought, 'I'll end this for good and all!' and threw himself into the foaming waters. But a passer-by saw him, plunged in after him and brought him safely to the river bank.

'Whatever did you do *that* for?' said the man, half-angry and yet concerned. Gabjir panted, 'Look at my hands!' He expected the man to strike him or to leave him at once in horror. But his rescuer spoke kindly: 'But even so why should you kill yourself?' Gabjir answered sadly, 'Because I am a leper, and my family has cast me out. I have no home, there's nothing to live for . . . and I don't know where to go.'

'But you must not give way to despair,' said the man very kindly. 'Haven't you heard of the hospital at Chandag Heights, just over the border in India?' 'No,' said Gabjir, 'I've never heard of the place.' 'Well *I* have,' said the man, 'and I know that if you go there you will be cared for and given everything you need.'

Gabjir looked puzzled: 'But why should strangers take me in when my own people have cast me out?' The man smiled and shrugged his shoulders, 'I don't know why they do it, but I've heard from those who have been there, and I know that they do.' He turned to go, and as he said goodbye he added: 'Mind you go to Chandag,' and was soon out of sight.

For a time Gabjir lay on the river bank in the sunshine while his clothes dried, and as he lay there he thought about the strange words of his rescuer. Could there really be a place where he would be welcomed and cared for? It sounded impossible. But as the day wore on and he felt better a faint flame of hope began to kindle in his mind, and he said to himself, 'I'll *go* to Chandag!' So he set out on his journey. He knew it would be difficult; in fact it was appalling. For more than four weeks he walked, climbed, crawled, up and down the rocky mountain tracks, through narrow valleys, and over steep ridges. Night after night he felt he could not go on any longer, but every morning the desire to reach Chandag spurred him on, and off he went once more. He slept wherever he happened to be at nightfall. He lived on whatever he could find on the bushes by the wayside, and the water from the mountain streams. His clothes wore out and he looked like a beggar in his rags. He became thinner and thinner. Whenever he had to pass through a village he asked whether he was on the right road for Chandag, and always they said 'yes', and pointed him on straight ahead. By the time that he had crossed the frontier of Nepal into India he could not walk any longer; his feet were hurting him too much. He could only crawl on his hands and knees, but now, every day, he could see the white buildings of Chandag up there on the hill; and each day he was a little nearer to his goal. At last, early in December, more dead than alive, he crawled into the garden of the doctor's bungalow and lay there on the ground in an exhausted heap. He could hardly lift his hands, for his hands and knees and feet were cut to the bone by that last effort to drag himself up the steep mountain path.

The doctor examined him, and at once sent for some of the stronger men among the patients to carry Gabjir down the hill a little way to the men's quarters. There he was fed and washed and his wounds were dressed. His rags were stripped off and burned, and he was given clean white garments. Then he was put to bed, to rest and recover. His welcome could not have been more friendly and compassionate, as well as efficient. But Gabjir was too worn out to notice. He accepted everything that was done for him without a word of thanks. Indeed he hardly seemed aware of his surroundings at all.

Gradually his physical health improved, though he was badly crippled by his disease. When he got up and began to move about the doctor and nurses and other patients tried to get into touch with him, but he gave such evasive answers that they thought it kinder to leave him alone. The other men did all they could to draw him into the life of the community, but he remained aloof and detached. He never smiled. He never thanked anybody for anything. When he was sufficiently recovered to walk a little way he was invited to come to the chapel every day for the Christian prayers. He went because he was asked, but he never showed any sign of interest. He was sunk in a pit of misery and depression where no one could reach him.

Then came Christmas Day! While it was still dark the carol-singers came round singing, 'Glory to the newborn King'. Gabjir was roused by the singing, but it did not mean anything to him, so he turned over and went to sleep again. Presently he heard one of the men calling to him: 'Gabjir, wake up! It's Christmas Day. We are all getting ready to go to church.' Mechanically he got up and dressed and went with the others to the church on the hill. Outside the sun had risen over the snow-covered mountains. The trees and bushes were glittering with frost. Inside the church there was colour and light and flowers and the singing was joyful and heartfelt. Many a man and woman far more badly crippled than Gabjir was singing with infectious gladness. Gabjir sat a little way apart from the other men, still sunk in his own misery. Obviously he did not notice what was happening. He might as well not have been there.

After the service the patients gathered in the hall for the present-giving. They all looked forward to this event for weeks beforehand, for they knew that friends from England had sent little gifts as personal presents for each one of them. The doctor went round distributing little cotton bags holding these gifts. When she came to Gabjir she put a little bag into his hands. He was so surprised he did not know what to make of it. He looked round to see what the others were doing and he saw that they were all opening their bags and exclaiming with pleasure. So, very gingerly, not knowing what to expect, he opened his bag, and drew out a brightly coloured woollen scarf and a cake of fragrant soap. He stared. Then he whispered to the man next to him: 'I say, what's all this about?' Then he looked down at the scarf and the cake of soap, and said wonderingly, 'Is all this for *me*?' 'Of course it is,' laughed his neighbour. 'Have you never had a Christmas present before?'

Gabjir looked perplexed, then he said slowly and thoughtfully, 'I've never had a *present* before . . . in all my life.' 'Well, now you have, and you know what it means, don't you?' said the other man. 'No,' said Gabjir, 'I don't understand it at all. Where did this scarf come from?' 'Why, from England, of course.' 'Who made it?' he enquired. 'I don't know; all I know is that these friends in England send us these presents every year.' 'Why?' said Gabjir. 'Why? Because Christians always give each other presents on Christmas Day, because on this day God our Father gave us the greatest gift of all, our Lord Jesus Christ,' he added reverently.

Gabjir sat there holding his scarf. Sometimes he turned it round and round and looked at it, as if it were not quite real. Suddenly, for the first time since he came to Chandag, he began to smile, and the smile lit up his face; he looked quite different. Like a man waking from a bad dream he looked round at his neighbours—all lepers like himself, but so friendly, and so happy, and he began to realize that they were friendly to him, and wanted him to be happy too. But what amazed him most of all was the fact that someone—a stranger— had *cared* enough to send *him* this beautiful present.

From that day forward Gabjir was a different person. He went regularly to the Christian prayers. He listened with great attention, and tried to understand what was being said and done. He began to talk with the other patients, and even began to say 'Thank you' to the nurses who looked after him, and to the doctor when she examined him. To his surprise, one morning about three weeks later, six men stood up at the end of the prayers and asked to be baptized: 'We want to become Christians', they said, 'because we know now that God loves us, and that Jesus is our Friend.' Gabjir was deeply impressed by what these men said. Some weeks later five of them were baptized. Gabjir watched the service with a great longing in his eyes. At the end of the service he suddenly called out, 'I too want to be baptized! I believe in Jesus Christ.'

During the weeks of preparation for baptism Gabjir showed by his life that he knew what he was doing. One day when the doctor went to a cottage in the men's quarters where a man was dying, in the last stages of leprosy—a terrible sight—she found Gabjir kneeling by the man's side, looking after him with the greatest kindness and compassion, in spite of the awful smell and the pitiful condition of the dying man. He was doing all he could to make him a little less uncomfortable. The doctor was so surprised that later on in the day she said to Gabjir: 'How is it that you, a high-caste man, can bring yourself to do things for that poor man who is of the lowest class?'

Gabjir smiled, 'Only in this way', he said, 'can I show the Lord Jesus how much I love him.'

Six months after Gabjir had crawled into the doctor's garden, looking as she said like a 'human derelict', he was baptized and made his first Communion. He took the name of Paul. It was a great day for him and for all the members of that suffering community. His face shone with joy as he answered the questions put to him and made his baptismal vows. No one who was present could ever forget the joy of that service. Paul was indeed 'a new man'. People who came to visit the hospital were so much impressed by his bearing and his appearance that they would ask: 'Who is that happy man?'

Two years later Paul came to the doctor with a request: 'May I go back to my own village to see my people?'

'Why do you want to go back to them, Paul Masih? You told us that they had said they would kill you if you went back.'

'Yes, doctor, I know they did,' he said, 'but still I want to go.'

'But although you are better, you still have the signs of leprosy upon you, and you are not fit to walk and climb; your feet are still deformed . . .'

'I know, Miss Sahib, but I want to go and tell them of my "Treasure". If I don't tell them of Christ who will? There is no one else, and I can't bear to think of them dying there without once hearing.'

'You know the risk you are taking?'

'Yes, but if you will let me I want to go.'

A few days later Paul said goodbye, and set out on his journey to Nepal. As he went through the white gate of the bungalow he turned round and said to the doctor, 'Don't worry! If I am still alive I will come back.'

But Paul never came back.

15 · Rama's Christmas

A Story from India

MANY years ago, in a remote village in South India, there lived a boy called Rama. It was his twelfth birthday, 24th December. He had been out all day, fishing, and as he walked home through the twilight his mind was full of his coming 'birthday treat'. Rama belonged to the *kallar* caste, sometimes called 'robbers': that is, men who were trained to make daring raids on distant villages. They would swoop down silently and unexpectedly upon a village, seize their booty, and vanish into the darkness before the astonished and frightened villagers had realized what was happening. These 'robbers' were very proud of their name. They regarded themselves as 'heroes', as daring brigands who could outwit anyone. Rama was feeling excited at the prospect of joining in a raid perhaps that very night. Never before had he been allowed to go out with the men on such a daring enterprise. But now he was twelve, almost grown-up. He saw himself as a 'hero', and longed to prove his mettle.

When he stepped through a gap in the thick hedge which surrounded his home village, he found all the men gathered in front of a small temple, dedicated to the god, Rama. The priest was offering prayers and sacrifices for the success of the raid. The men watched him anxiously. At last he turned towards them and said solemnly: 'Yes, the omens are favourable; you may go forth.' At once all the men joined in a song of praise to Rama, the Divine Hero.

Then they went back to their homes, made their final preparations for the raid, said goodbye to their wives and set out.

They did not go in a body. As soon as they reached the forest they divided into little groups, sometimes only in twos and threes. They slipped in and out among the trees, moving silently in the darkness. Rama walked with his father. It was a fine night, warm and clear, and the stars were shining brightly in the night sky; but under the trees the shadows were black. As they wound their way in and out among the trees, Rama said to his father: 'Father, why did you choose this particular night for the raid?' With a mischievous glance at his father's face he added, ' It wasn't because it's my birthday, I suppose?' His father smiled. 'No, my son, it wasn't.' Then he went on, in a low voice: 'The village we are going to attack tonight is a Christian village, and we know that tonight they are holding a special festival. This means that they will all be in their temple, so we can dash into the village, seize the booty, and be off again before they are any the wiser.'

Rama was silent for a few moments; then he said : 'I wonder what their festival is like. Do you think we could watch it from a safe place?' His father reflected for a moment, then he said : 'Yes, so far as I am concerned you can—and I'll come with you; we've plenty of time.'

Rama's father whispered to the others who were passing at the moment and they nodded their assent. They passed the word to the rest, so by the time the raiders were near the village, they were all fairly close to one another. Without making a sound the men followed Rama and his father, who crept up to the wall of the church. Light was streaming through the open windows, making the darkness outside still deeper. Rama peered in first and his father followed. They could see and hear everything. The building was packed with people—men, women and children, and even babies—all sitting on the floor. It was a cheerful scene. Garlands of coloured paper were stretched across the building from side to side, and every ledge and corner was gay with flowers. All the people had on their best clean clothes and looked very happy. In the front of the church there stood a green tree in a wooden tub, sparkling with what looked like gold and silver streamers. At that moment, everyone was listening with great attention to the man who stood before them, near the tree, reading from a large book. And as Rama listened he was astonished, for this is what he heard:

'The people that sat in darkness have seen a great light, they that dwell in the land of the shadow of death, upon them hath the light shined . . . thou hast increased their joy: they joy before thee according to the joy in harvest, *as men rejoice when they divide the spoil.*'

The 'robbers' looked at one another in amazement. *They* knew this 'joy'; that was how they felt after every successful raid, but what on earth did these words mean here? The next words sounded stranger still:

'For all the armour of the armed man, and the tumult and the garments rolled in blood, shall even be for burning, for fuel of fire.'

In their own experience these men knew the meaning of these words only too well.

They all crept closer to the windows in order to hear some more. The reader continued: 'For unto us a child is born . . .' Then came some strange words about a Hero who seemed to be a kind of Deliverer, but he was to be called a 'Prince of Peace'. These last words shocked them all. Rama felt indignant. 'Peace', he thought to himself, *'that's* not what we want. *We* are heroes.' Yet these strange words disturbed them all, and as they slipped away into the darkness the words haunted them. Most of the raiders felt uneasy, and several were afraid. But Rama stayed at the window; he could not tear himself away. Then the Christians began to sing, and their singing went to Rama's heart; it was so joyful and so free.

Then the man went on reading out of the book. It sounded like a sort of prophecy, something more about a great De-liverer. Rama listened with all his might, but the next moment he was shocked by the words:

'They shall beat their swords into ploughshares, and their spears into pruning-hooks: nation shall not lift up sword against nation, *neither shall they learn war any more.*'

At this moment Rama's father touched him and signed to him to come away. Just then the Christians were startled by the hoarse cry of a parakeet close at hand. But Rama knew that this was the leader's signal, so he hurried off with his father to the prearranged meeting-place. But in his heart Rama was disappointed. 'Why had they withdrawn into the jungle?' he wondered. 'When was the raid going to begin?' But he dared not speak to his father, who looked stern and uneasy. When they met the whole group, a fierce argument was going on. Some wanted to go on with the raid, but several others were against it. 'There's something uncanny here,' said one man, 'and I for one don't want to get mixed up with any strange magic.'

Now it was a rule in this caste that they must never make a raid unless they were all agreed. Since there was so much difference of opinion, the leader closed the discussion by saying shortly: 'We are not of one mind, so that's that. It's off!'

In the months that followed this strange experience Rama thought a great deal about that village, and what he had heard there. But he always felt uncomfortable when the other boys taunted him about 'the raid that never came off'. One day he happened to overhear two women talking. They had just come back from a trip to the nearest town and they were full of news. 'Do you know', said one of them to her friend, 'I hear that in that Christian village they even have a school for boys?'

Now if there was one thing that Rama wanted more than anything else it was to go to school. There were no schools in his neighbourhood, and he had been feeling quite hopeless about it. The moment that he heard about this school he went to his father and told him. Then he talked about it to his mother. Both his parents listened to him and tried to understand why he was so excited about it. No one they knew sent their boys to school and why should Rama want it? But he pestered them with questions and kept on coming back to the subject: 'Why can't I go to school?' At last they gave way. Rama's father went off to the village and asked to see the 'schoolmaster'. He was directed to a small white bungalow near the little church (which was also the school). After a long conversation with the white man (the European missionary) Rama's father agreed to send his boy to the school at the beginning of the following term. It was arranged that Rama should become a boarder as the distance was too great to go to and fro daily. 'But', said the headmaster, 'there are long holidays, and in the great heat he will be at home for several weeks.' So it was all settled, and Rama was delighted.

When the next Christmas came round Rama had been at the school for several months. He was very happy there. Full of delight at the thought of the approaching festival Rama went out into the forest with the older boys to find and cut down a Casuarina tree for the church. Proudly they brought it back, planted it in the green tub and decorated its drooping green branches—with their little cones—with all kinds of fine silver and golden streamers. Rama enjoyed learning the Christmas carols. There was one he liked best of all. It did not sound 'foreign', as some of them did; it was set to a familiar Indian tune (in honour of Rama) and the refrain was sung with great vigour: 'Vandar! Vandar! He comes, he comes.' Like the others Rama was allowed to choose a verse of Scripture to recite at the service on Christmas Eve. He chose the words of Isaiah ending with the phrase, 'Neither shall there be war any more'. When he stood up and recited these words in his turn at the festival service everyone looked at him with great interest (for they knew that he came from the *kallar* caste) and the minister looked at him with astonishment. When the service was over the minister spoke to Rama alone with great kindness. Rama was so deeply moved that he could not speak. He ran out into the forest and wandered about among the trees in a tumult of mixed feelings. He felt sad and yet happy, and he could not understand himself. And as he wandered along the narrow path with his mind in ferment a parakeet flew overhead screeching.

When the great heat of summer began, the school broke up for the long holidays. Rama went home, delighted to think of seeing his parents, and his brothers and sisters, and all the other friends in the village. But after the first few days, when the excitement had died down, he began to feel restless and

unhappy. He did not know why. He felt as if he were being torn in two between two worlds, the world of home and the world of school and the Christian village. Soon his mother noticed his uneasiness. She guessed what was troubling him, and she went straight to the point. She talked to him quietly and lovingly about the difference between the two 'worlds'. 'You mustn't think we don't have our beautiful festivals, too,' she said. 'Don't you remember what happy times we had together when you were younger?' Rama nodded his head, but he still looked unhappy. 'Perhaps you've forgotten what they are like?' added his mother, but she did not press the point any further.

Soon after this conversation came the usual celebrations of the Krishna Festival[1] in his own village. That morning Rama was roused very early by a great deal of noise outside. He jumped up and saw his mother and his sisters carrying great brass vessels full of water from the village well. Then the whole family gathered round the household altar and his father solemnly sprinkled them all with holy water as he walked three times round the room. Then he turned towards the little blue image of Krishna on the altar and made a vow, in the name of them all, that this day they would all fast from morning till evening in honour of Krishna. After that the whole

[1] *Krishna Jayanti*, in honour of the birth of Krishna—a public holiday throughout India.

H

family went out to the village bathing-pool, accompanied by the rest of the village. The girls handed round flasks of sesame oil with which everyone anointed his head, arms and the upper part of the body. As the sun rose over the water they all stepped into the pool and dipped three times in order to be free from the sin of the three births.

The rest of the day was spent very pleasantly. The whole village was *en fête*. The children played games, the elders sat in the shade and talked or slept, the young men and women brought flowers and branches to decorate the Krishna shrine; they wove garlands of flowers and hung them on the trees, which surrounded the sacred place, they scattered flowers on the ground before the shrine.

As darkness fell, all gathered round the shrine and sang a special hymn in honour of Krishna. By the light of the moon more hymns were sung, while the air was fragrant with the scent of incense. Then the whole group became quite silent. Later, scenes from the life of Krishna were acted by a number of the younger people. More singing followed. After a festive meal, a great noise was made to drive away the evil spirits. It was past midnight when people began to stroll back to their homes. But Rama could not sleep. The whole festival, which he had always enjoyed so much as a child, had lost its charm. He got up and slipped out of the house and walked up and down among the trees. He was thinking hard. He now realized that much as he loved his family and his home, at some vital point he had grown away from them. This made him very unhappy. 'Whatever shall I do?' he asked himself; and there seemed to be no answer.

After the summer holidays Rama went back to school. During the weeks of uncertainty he had come to a decision. He knew that the only course for him was to ask for Christian baptism. He told his parents. They were amazed and distressed. After a good deal of argument they gave a reluctant consent. He hated giving his parents so much trouble and disappointment, but he knew that it was only due to the fact that they could not understand why he wanted to take this step. As

Christmas came near he was glad to know that soon his private decision would be made public, for he was to receive baptism, with five older boys, at the Christmas Eve service itself. He joined in all the preparations with a quiet joy, though the pain of his parents' disapproval often weighed on his heart.

The great day came at last. Rama stood before the minister with the other five boys. When it came to his turn the minister said: 'I baptize thee, Samthanavira (hero of peace) in the Name of the Father and of the Son and of the Holy Ghost'; and then he added: 'How beautiful upon the mountains are the feet of them that bring the good news of peace.'

Samthanavira's heart was full of joy. Yet as he rose to go back to his seat he glanced at his parents and a pang went through him. His mother was sitting on the very back bench weeping bitterly. Outside, looking in through the window, stood his father with a look of grim disapproval, so forbidding that it cut the boy to the heart.

Many years passed. Rama—to use his old name—had now become a Christian pastor himself. He lived in a small village far from the home of his childhood. He was about to conduct the Christmas Service, but this time everything had changed. His heart was overflowing with joy, for many kallars, from his own caste, had become staunch Christians. Best of all, on this Christmas Day, his parents were with him, now full members of the Church, and all their hopes for him, they now knew, had been realized in another and better way, the way of peace.

16 · *The Conquest of Fear*

A True Story from Basutoland

THERE was great excitement in a number of little villages scattered about on the mountain side in a beautiful valley in the heart of Africa. The villagers, many of them pagan, were busy getting ready to go down to the big village in the valley to 'keep Christmas'. They were not very sure what it was all about, but people who had been there the year before said it was 'wonderful' and 'everyone ought to go'. The weather was very hot, and the sun shone down upon a cluster of huts at the end of the large village below. Everyone knew the house at the corner, for it belonged to the Christian teacher, a young widow. She was always known as 'Daniel's wife', for Daniel had been the leading Christian man in the village, and he had died a year before.

It was Christmas Eve, and in other years all the people of the village, Christian and pagan alike, had joined in a great festival. But today everything was very quiet at that end of the village, for everyone knew that Daniel's wife had just lost her little boy John. So no one was sitting under the trees, no one was singing, no children were running about or calling to each other from the surrounding huts.

A little way off down the street stood the school house; inside, the young African assistant teacher was standing looking at the Christmas tree she was supposed to be decorating. It was planted in a tin filled with earth, but it looked very awkward because it could not stand up straight, and how was she to put candles on a tree in such a position? She was sure they would fall off. This was the first time she had been asked to decorate the tree, for last year this was done by Daniel's wife herself.

A few children were standing outside the school-house looking in through the door, but they were unusually quiet and subdued. They were talking together in low voices: 'Do you think we'll have a Christmas tree at all this year?' 'Oh yes!' said one child, 'We shall. Look, Priscilla is there beginning the decorations!' But she added, 'It won't be the same if Daniel's wife isn't there.'

'Isn't she going to be here?' said another. 'Why—of course not,' said the first child. 'How could she be here? She must mourn, for Little John only died last night.' The children were silent for a moment and then one little girl said importantly, 'When my brother died we built up the wall and made a new door.' The others were impressed, but a small Christian spoke up: 'Whatever did you do that for?' The others laughed at her. 'Don't you *know*?' they exclaimed. 'It's to prevent the spirits of evil from getting into the house.' The little Christian girl shivered slightly, then she answered boldly: 'But there aren't any evil spirits now.' 'But there *are*,' said the other child. 'My father says that they have only hidden themselves away for a time.' 'But', said the Christian child, 'the angels are stronger than the evil spirits,' and then one or two, more courageous than the rest, joined in; they nodded their heads and said, 'Yes, she's right! The angels are much stronger!'

During this conversation the children had been sitting on the ground in the shade of a great tree, but suddenly they all scrambled to their feet for Daniel's wife was standing before them. They looked up at her with curiosity, and a little embarrassment. She looked just as usual; she was wearing her blue cotton dress and her apron, and her black scarf on her head. When she saw that the children were silent from embarrassment she smiled at them and laid her hand reassuringly upon the head of the little pagan girl. Then she spoke to the children: 'Now I want you all to go home and tell your parents that this evening we shall have our Christmas Festival. At one hour before sunset the bell will be rung three times. After the third time we shall begin.' A smile of relief stole over their faces, coupled with an expression of wondering expectation. Then off they went to their homes to give the news.

Daniel's wife then went on down the street to the school. She walked into the schoolhouse and spoke to Priscilla. 'I've come to help you,' she said very quietly. Priscilla turned round with a startled expression on her face, and then said slowly: 'But no one will come!' Daniel's wife put down a candle-holder on to the table and said, 'What do you mean, Priscilla . . . no one will come?' After a short silence she added, 'Do you really believe that they are *afraid* because of little John?' 'They're not frightened of *him*,' said Priscilla, 'but they say the spirits of the ancestors are angry with *you*, and that's why they have taken away from you, first your husband and then your son. It's the wrath of the ancestors being poured out upon you because you haven't offered the usual sacrifices.' She faltered for a moment, and then said rather awkwardly, 'Well, you see, that's what the pagans think!'

Daniel's wife listened in silence, then she said firmly: 'Well, Priscilla, I'm afraid I must leave *you* to get on with the tree and the decorations after all, for I see I have other things to do. Have you practised the carols with the schoolchildren? Oh! and when the teacher from Boluwedu comes to take the service this evening, mind you look after him well, and give him something to eat!'

Then Daniel's wife went back to her house. Inside it was dim and cool, for although it was not built in the usual African fashion but was rather European in style, the thatched roof came down very far beyond the little windows so that no sunlight could get into the house. In the centre of the room stood a low camp-bed covered by a rug; on it lay the body of little John, who had been running about in perfect health only a few days ago, as merry as a cricket. But an acute attack of malaria had carried him off, in spite of all the expert care given him by the doctor-missionary from Medingen—even she could not help him. There he lay, his little brown face very peaceful, almost happy. His little hands lay clasped on the white sheet.

His mother was bending over him, when she felt something solid on the floor, close to her feet. She looked down and said gently, 'Is that you Maria?' Maria did not answer; she sat there huddled up with her chin on her knees and her thin arms clasped round her little feet. She was gazing up into the face of her little brother, lost in a maze of bewilderment. She seemed to be in a fantastic dream. Was she thinking about John? Wouldn't they ever play together any more? The mother laid her hand gently on the little curly head: 'Go down to the school darling, and help Priscilla. She has such a lot to do and she needs you; you can be a great help to her, you know.' The child still sat there gazing at her brother, then she said, 'But Mother, I don't want to go to the school. I want to mourn.'

'But today it's Christmas,' said her mother, very firmly, 'and Christians don't mourn on Christmas Day. We all want to hear the angels singing, "Behold, I bring you good tidings of great joy!" Tomorrow there will be time to mourn, but not today: it's Christmas.' The little girl looked up wonderingly at her mother whose eyes were shining. She was surprised; only half understanding her mother's words she got up obediently from the floor and went out into the sunshine.

Daniel's wife was just getting ready to go out when she saw a shadow in the doorway. There stood two strange men who were peering into the room, but when they saw her they turned and were about to pass on. But she beckoned them to come inside. 'Why do you want to run away?' she asked. She spoke with authority and the men looked at her uneasily. At last one of them said, 'But you are mourning.' 'No,' she answered, 'I am not mourning.' Then the other man said: 'But surely you aren't going to have a festival in the school this evening, are you?'

'Certainly, we shall hold the festival just as usual,' she replied. 'The teacher from Boluwedu is coming and will conduct the service, and the school children are going to sing and celebrate the festival of great joy. You are all invited.' The men were so confused and awed that they went away quietly without speaking.

A few minutes later, as she was getting ready to go out again, she heard someone else calling to her. She went to the door and looked out: there stood an old woman leaning on a stick. She called out, 'You, Daniel's wife, now do you see how dangerous it is to neglect the ancestors? First you lost your husband and now your only son. Go!' she shrieked, 'call in the witch doctor and ask him to offer sacrifice. If you don't you'll lose your last surviving child. Aren't you afraid?' she shouted in a threatening voice. Then she came quite close up to Daniel's wife and looked her in the face: 'Aren't you afraid?'

Daniel's wife looked at the old woman very kindly and smiled: her dark eyes were shining as she looked right into the angry eyes of the old woman. Then she laid her hand in deep compassion upon the woman's shoulder, 'No, Mother,' she said, 'I'm not afraid.' Then, as a little crowd had gathered to hear what was going on, she added: 'No, I'm not afraid, my son is with God, and there he is happy and safe. I shall go to him, and one day I shall see him and Daniel once more. Can't you see how happy this makes us who are Christians? Ah, but it is you who are to be pitied! Come to us tonight and join in our festival, and you will see how you can be set free from fear.'

The old woman hobbled away muttering to herself. And the other people went off in another direction.

After that more and more people strolled past the hut and each time Daniel's wife called out to them to invite them to the Christmas Festival that night. And they in their turn went away into the bush villages and spread the news. The people were amazed: 'And do you mean to say that Daniel's wife is not mourning, and that she has invited us all to the Festival of Joy?' 'Yes, indeed it's for us all!' The others shook their heads in bewilderment and asked: 'So you mean to say that she is not afraid?' 'No, she isn't afraid.' And many said, 'Well, we must go and see this great thing—her son dead, and she bids us rejoice! This is a strange magic.'

Up in the hills in a little village a very old man was sitting in his hut. Suddenly he heard the voices of women talking excitedly, so he went to the door to listen, and he wondered at what they were saying. Then he called out to them and questioned them : 'Is all this true that you are saying?' 'Yes, indeed, for we have seen Daniel's wife with our own eyes, and we have spoken with her.' 'And is it true that she is not afraid?'

'Quite true,' they said. When the women had left the old man went to speak with his son: 'You must come down with me into that village this evening! I have never seen a Christian Festival. I want to see if it's true that they are not afraid.'

That evening, an hour before sunset, the Bell rang, three times. And from the hills above and from all the surrounding bush villages little groups of people came eagerly and silently towards the Christian school-house. Men, women and children came from the heathen villages. Such a number had never come before. They came to celebrate the joy of Christmas, with little John.

17 · Stars in the Night

MABEL SHAW

A True Story from Rhodesia

'*And they shall come from the East and from the West, and from the North, and from the South, and shall sit down in the kingdom of God*'—Luke 13.29.

IT was Christmas Eve. In the school compound a great crowd of people sat in silence. They had come from villages across the river and plains, for the word had gone forth that once again, this year, the manner of the Great Chief's coming was going to be made known.

Two great fires lit up one end of the yard, and here and there golden lamps made a ring of light; and overhead the moon and the stars shone in the dark sky. But it was towards the *nsaka* in the centre that all eyes were turned, for that held the great Light: four large golden lamps stood as sentinels on either side of a low couch, on which reclined a woman, her eyes fixed on a low trough in which a little child lay on a bed of soft grass. A man sat near the couch, warming his hands over a fire of sticks, and on the other side a woman knelt grinding flour. In the background there were sheep and goats lying asleep on the straw. And from that little round *nsaka* the light streamed out into the big courtyard.

Presently the sound of far-away singing came like a wind from the forest, and the stillness deepened. The singing came nearer, and Joseph left his little fire and went out and looked up into the starlit sky. The woman stopped her grinding, sat back on her heels, and looked wonderingly at the mother. But Mary looked only towards the little child. The woman rose, and bending low, went to the baby, lifted him up, and gave him into his mother's arms, and for a time she knelt there, watching.

The singing was now very near, all about them it seemed, and it startled some shepherds sleeping round one of the big fires. Two of them jumped up in alarm, looked wildly round, and then woke their fellows.

As they stood there, mystified, afraid, from the darkness came a tall figure in robes of white and gold, bearing aloft a star of golden light. The shepherds fell on their faces, the singing dropped to a whisper, and through it came the clear voice of the angel, 'Fear not, for behold I bring you good tidings of great joy . . .' The shepherds lifted their heads and looked towards the place where the angel was pointing, and then bowed in awe once more for the light about them was very bright. Other angels had come, bearing their stars of light and with them came little child-angels with golden wings outspread, dancing before them, the bells on their ankles keeping time with the swelling music.

And while the unseen choir told the story, the shepherds rose, went towards the *nsaka*, and bending low, entered and knelt there wondering, worshipping. Then one of the men left his fellows, drew near to the Mother and Child: he knelt with his forehead to the earth, his companions joined him. At length they rose, and with many backward looks, returned, talking with each other in whispers.

As they disappeared into the darkness, the music changed, and from the east came three regal figures, their faces lifted to the starry heavens. Slowly they came, carrying precious gifts, tall, dignified, serene, in robes of royal colours, with jewelled turbans on their heads. They entered the *nsaka*, made lowly obeisance, and laid them at his feet. A great hush came over the whole company, as if all present were joining in that act of adoration.

Once more the kings made their obeisance and left the

nsaka; silently and reverently they moved away. As they neared the shadows they turned, lifted their arms as if hailing the Light of Light, to which the star had led them, and then withdrew once more into the darkness. And a sigh like a great wind stirred among the people.

Once more the music changed, and now it was gay, sweet music such as children love, and into the light they came: little children dancing, carrying red and blue flowers. They met at the *nsaka* and knelt there, and greeted their King as Africa does, by bending forward and clapping. Then they rose, and sang about the flowers they had brought—the blue of royalty and the crimson glowing rose of love. They took their flowers, following one another into the *nsaka* and each child knelt to place her flower before him. Then, singing and dancing, back they went into the darkness.

Again the scene changed: from all sides came draped figures, protecting little faint candlelights in their hands. They represented those who, from all quarters of the earth, guided by the 'Light that lighteth every man', for ever seek until they find the Light of Light.

The music died into silence as slowly they converged upon the *nsaka*. They knelt in a semi-circle on the threshold, placed their little flickering lights before them and sang of their search, of their triumph in finding, and worshipped and adored.

Now came the triumphant music of a great army on the march—and a long procession came into sight: it was as if the morning stars sang together for joy at the approach of day, for all carried stars of golden light. The angels led the way, then came the shepherds, the kings, the children, and at the end, the seekers—a long procession of golden stars.

The watching crowd held its breath as the procession came nearer and nearer and surrounded the *nsaka*. The children carried their star-lamps as if they were holy things, and the light lit up their rapt faces. Round and round they went, singing their welcome and their joy. It was the great hymn of the faithful of all ages and of many races: '*O come, all ye faithful*'. When they came to the last verse, 'Yea, Lord, we greet thee', there was a pause, and they moved to form one vast circle. Then all knelt on the ground, placing their stars before them, thus surrounding the *nsaka* with a ring of light. When they had finished there was a great sound of clapping: this time everyone joined in, not only the children, but the old men and women in that vast audience were kneeling on the ground and clapping.

After a brief silence the children rose to their feet, picked up their lamps, and walked slowly back in procession, singing as they went, 'like silver lamps in a distant shrine'. When the smaller children had disappeared into the darkness the leaders came to the centre, knelt and lifted their lamps on high while they sang softly, 'Jesu, Word of God Incarnate'. Then they too rose, leaving their lamps on the ground which formed a Cross, outlined in light.

Before a sound broke the deep stillness the six angels appeared once more but without lights. They walked into the centre and sang, as a prayer for the whole world: 'Saviour, sprinkle many nations'.

NOTES AND ACKNOWLEDGMENTS

1 *The Emperor's Vision.* This story has been taken from *Christ Legends*, a translation from the Swedish, published in England in 1930, but it has been considerably shortened and adapted. The author, Selma Lagerlöf (1858-1940), received the Nobel Prize for Literature in 1909.

2 *The First Christmas Tree* by Will Vesper. The source of this story is a small collection of Christmas legends and stories entitled *Frohe Weihnacht Überall*. Its original title is *Die Verirrten Wanderer*. No date is given, and I cannot trace this story further back.

3 *The Holy Night* by Selma Lagerlöf. Taken from the same book as No. 1.

4 *Christmas Eve on the Mountain* by Adalbert Stifter. Retold, in shortened form, from the famous story by Adalbert Stifter (1805-1868), now regarded as Austria's greatest prose writer. 'His style has been compared with the music of Mozart and Schubert.' The original title was *Der Heilige Abend*, later altered to *Bergkristall*. It appears in almost all modern German collections for Christmas, and can be read in full in Harrap's Bilingual Series (1950), under the title *Bergkristall* (Rock Crystal). The present adaptation of this story is used by courtesy of Verlag der Arche—Peter Schifferli of Zürich.

5 *The Avalanche* by Hanne Menken. Retold, in a much shortened version, from a small book by Hanne Menken entitled *Christnacht im Schnee*. Its date is 1935, but it has been impossible to trace the publisher.

6 *The Christmas Mail* by A. de Meck. This story was published by the SCM Press in 1945 as a small book for children.

7 *Santa Risolina* by Heinrich Federer. This story has been adapted from a much longer version (in German) written by Heinrich Federer (1866-1928), a well-known, poetic Swiss writer, who had a great love for Italy; to him it was 'like a

second home'. Permission has been given for the use of this story by G. Grote'sche Verlagsbuchhandlung of Cologne and Berlin.

8 *Long Ago in Norway* by Sigrid Undset. The writer of this story, Sigrid Undset (1882-1949), was a Norwegian with close links with Denmark and Scotland. During the German occupation of Norway her books were banned by the Nazis. She escaped to America in 1941 but was able to return home after the war. Several of her longer novels are already well known in this country (in translation). The original title of this story —which shows her interest in the pre-Reformation period in her own country—was *Christmas Peace*.

9 *An Exile's Story* by Nikolai S. Lesskov (1831-1895). Lesskov is regarded as one of the most original of nineteenth century Russian writers. His complete works occupy 36 volumes. Many of these have been translated into German, and are well known. The story which is translated from *Der Gast beim Bauern* is used by permission of Paulus Verlag of Recklinghausen.

10 *The Sacrifice* by Henri Bordeaux. This short story comes from the pen of a prolific French writer, Henri Bordeaux; it is taken from a collection of 'Contes Savoyards' which he wrote early in his long career. I have translated it from the original French in a small book, *Choix des Nouvelles modernes*, published for school use in Germany in Bielefeld and Leipzig in 1923 and kindly lent to me by a Swiss schoolmaster, Herr Rudolf Weckerle.

11 *The Three Dark Kings* by Wolfgang Borchert (1921-1947). The writer suffered a great deal during his short life. His writings reveal his compassion and distress about conditions in post-war Germany.

12 *The Christ-Child of Ostrowice* by Friedrich Hoffmann. This poignant little fragment is evidently based on firsthand knowledge of what happened in Poland during the war. It is used by permission of J. F. Steinkopf Verlag, Stuttgart.

13 *Christmas in Prison* by Hanns Lilje. This incident comes from *The Valley of the Shadow* by the Bishop of Hannover. This translation was published by the SCM Press in 1950. The original German title is *Im finstern Tal* (Lätare Verlag 1947).

14 *Gabjir's First Present*. This story is based upon facts, related in a booklet by Katharine Young, *Lengthen thy Cords*, and published by the Mission to Lepers in 1952. She is the *doctor* in the story. The Mission to Lepers also gave me a great deal of help with background material.

15 *Rama's Christmas* by Gustav Stählin. This story comes from a small booklet of three Christmas stories entitled *Uns ist ein Kind Geboren*. I have retold it in close dependence on the original German text, for which permission has kindly been given by the Furche Verlag of Hamburg.

16 *The Conquest of Fear*. This story comes from a German Lutheran paper entitled *Das Baugerüst*, No. 12, 1953. The story itself, however, comes from a very early period in the work of the Leipziger Mission in Basutoland. This mountainous country is surrounded by the Republic of South Africa; it is very progressive, especially in the sphere of education (which is largely in the hands of the Church, through Roman Catholic, French Reformed and Anglican missions). Its standard of literacy is very high—some say the highest in Africa.

17 *Stars in the Night* by Mabel Shaw. This story also comes from an early period in missions; but there is a prophetic quality about it which makes it timeless. This account is taken from *Dawn in Africa* (Livingstone Press, 1927).

Note: The Compiler wishes to express her warm thanks to all who have helped her in the preparation of this book by the loan of books or papers, or in other ways. She has made strenuous efforts to trace the source of the stories used and she begs indulgence if she has unwittingly infringed any copyright.